PEARSON SCIENCE 1 & 2

PROGRAM OVERVIEW

PEARSON

Feedback on this publication can be sent to editorialfeedback@pearsoned.com.

Pearson Canada Inc.
26 Prince Andrew Place
Don Mills, ON M3C 2T8
Customer Service: 1-800-361-6128

6 17
Printed and bound in Canada

The development team wishes to thank the following people:
Dr. Glen S. Aikenhead
Linda Aspen-Baxter
Judy Bear, Traditional Knowledge Keeper, Sweetgrass First Nation
Dr. Herman Michell
Rhonda Phillips
Ted View
The Saskatchewan Ministry of Education

Publisher: Reid McAlpine
Managing Editor: Lee Ensor
Developmental Editor: Eileen Pyne-Rudzik, Ph.D.
Editorial Assistant: Holly Robertson
Copy Editor: Linda Jenkins
Manager, Project Management K–12: Alison Dale
Project Manager, Production: Cheri Westra
Art Director: Zena Denchik
Cover Design: Alex Li
Cover Images: (left) © Shutterstock/Alena Brozova, (right) © Shutterstock/David Crockett
Interior Design: Carolyn E. Sebestyen
Composition: Computer Composition of Canada Inc.
Vice-President, K–12 Product Development: Mark Cobham

Illustrations: p. 8 Courtesy of the Saskatchewan Ministry of Education; p. 41 Word & Image Design Studio Inc.; p. 42 Word & Image Design Studio Inc.; p. 43 Word & Image Design Studio Inc.; p. 66 Courtesy of Knowledge Keeper Judy Bear; p. 85, 93, 94, 95, 96, 99, 100 Lapiz Digital Services, India

PEARSON

ISBN: 978-0-13-384419-1

Program Overview

. Using the *Pearson Science* Program in Your Classroom

2. Assessment and Evaluation

3. Fostering Scientific Knowledge

4. Helping Students Relate Science and Technology to the World Outside the School

5. Encouraging Responsible Attitudes in Science

6. Generic Line Masters

1 Using the *Pearson Science* Program in Your Classroom

Using the *Pearson Science 1 and 2 Teacher's Resources*

The *Pearson Science 1 and 2 Teacher's Resources* provide all of the tools you need to implement the *Pearson Science 1–2* program. Information is provided to help you plan each unit before you start.

- A Unit Indicators Correlation Chart itemizes where each outcome and indicator is covered in the lesson activities. Opportunities for ongoing assessment are listed to prepare you for assessing students as they work through the unit.
- A Unit Planning Chart shows the type(s) of activity in each lesson, overall time required to complete the activities in the lesson, suggestions for how to break the time and activities into more manageable chunks, materials needed for the activity, and the program masters or line masters you will need.

The **Unit Opener: Getting Started**

- provides a margin box that lists the estimated time and unit resources (i.e., posters, fiction and non-fiction Little Books, line or program masters)
- briefly explains the concepts and skills that students will learn over the course of the unit, all of which directly correlate with the outcomes and indicators in the curriculum
- introduces students to the Big Ideas/Essential Questions of the unit. You may choose to use the unit poster, which highlights aspects of the unit through photographs, diagrams, and questions to stimulate discussion. Alternatively, you could use an introductory activity and the creation of an ongoing bulletin-board display called an "I Wonder …" wall. This introduction asks students to come up with a set of "I Wonder …" statements that reflect their wonderings about the focus and content of the unit. Key "I Wonder …" statements are provided in the Teacher's Resource. Suggestions are provided to guide you in eliciting these "I Wonder …" statements from students and in setting up an "I Wonder …" wall in the classroom where students can post their statements, visual records of their explorations, and findings as they progress through the unit. The "I Wonder …" statements form a key component in the inquiry approach that is integrated into the activities in this Teacher's Resource. Return to students' "I Wonder …" statements at regular intervals throughout the unit to reflect on which ones have been addressed, which ones still need to be explored, and whether there are any new "I Wonder …" statements that need to be added. This reinforces the cyclical nature of inquiry learning that

begins with what students wonder about and want to learn and, after explorations and investigations, returns to the initial wonderings to reflect, assess, and wonder still more based on what has been learned.
- helps you assess students' prior knowledge
- introduces students to the fiction and non-fiction Little Books for the unit using before, during, and after reading strategies
- introduces students to the learning targets in student-friendly language
- provides appropriate tips, assessment checks, literacy checks, and safety checks in the margins

Each **Lesson**
- shows the approximate overall time the lesson takes
- lists the vocabulary introduced
- lists the line masters and program resources (e.g., unit posters, skills posters, Traditional Knowledge posters, fiction and non-fiction Little Books) that accompany the lesson
- lists any required materials and equipment for the activities
- lists the goal of the lesson
- provides an **Assessment Chart** that lists the Science and English Language Arts indicators that are addressed in the lesson and the activities in which each one is addressed
- offers **Background Information** that provides science background tha goes beyond the content of the lessons for the non-specialist teacher. This section also includes Traditional Knowledge, where appropriate. Traditional Knowledge is identified with an icon in the margin.
- provides assessment tips for ongoing assessment in an **Assessment *for* Learning** chart. This chart provides questions to guide you as you look for evidence of student learning. It also provides learning targets in student-friendly language.
- lists indicators from other disciplines that are addressed in the lesson in **Curriculum Connections**
- provides suggestions for how to differentiate instruction for students with different needs (EAL, Enrichment, Extra Support) in **Differentiating Instruction**
- provides teaching notes for **Core Learning Opportunities** that are broken into three subsections — **Engage**, **Explore**, and **Explain**:
  - The Engage section typically includes two subsections:
    - Activate and Build on Prior Knowledge: The purpose of these activities is to motivate, introduce, and stimulate the sharing of personal connections and background knowledge.
    - Develop "I Wonder …" Statements. The purpose is to elicit queries about the content and focus of the lesson.
  - The Explore section focuses on explorations and investigations in which students are actively involved in the inquiry process, gathering information, discovering answers, and/or gaining insights. During these hands-on activities, students will use and develop science vocabulary, science skills, key understandings, and scientific attitudes. The fiction and non-fiction Little Books may be

incorporated into Explore activities. When they are used, before, during, and after reading strategies may be incorporated.
  - The Explain section provides further active learning experiences with a greater focus on sharing what students learned during the Explore activities. Activities in this section focus on the demonstration of student learning and understanding. The fiction and non-fiction Little Books may be incorporated into Explain activities, as appropriate. When they are used, before, during, and after reading strategies may be incorporated.
- provides margin notes that include Science Checks (what to watch for in students to check for understanding; includes content, skills, processes, and attitudes), Literacy Checks (what to watch for as evidence of student progress in connection with ELA indicators), Safety Checks, Notes/Tips (additional information about activities), and icons to signify the use of technology and Traditional Knowledge
- provides **Alternate Learning Opportunities** in the form of an **Activity Bank**. This section provides optional activities for you to choose from to replace or supplement the Core Learning Opportunities and to meet students' needs, abilities, and interests. These activities provide additional opportunities to practise, apply, and extend the indicators for the lesson. They involve a variety of learning modalities, ability levels, and curricular connections.

The **Unit Closer: Putting It All Together**

- includes a margin box that lists the estimated time, unit resources, materials, and equipment
- provides teaching notes for **Looking Back**, which is broken into four subsections:
  - Consider the Learning Targets returns students to the learning targets from the start of the unit and has them rate their learning.
  - Complete/Reread the Fiction Book returns students to the Little Book for this unit and incorporates reading strategies.
  - Complete/Reread the Non-fiction Book also returns students to the Little Book for this unit and incorporates reading strategies.
  - Consider "I Wonder …" Queries returns students to the "I Wonder …" statements they made over the course of the unit and asks them to reflect on and share their learning with a partner. This subsection also suggests that you may wish to co-plan inquiry investigations with your students for any "I Wonder …" queries that have not been answered.
- provides a Unit Task in **Going Further** that challenges students to use what they have learned during the unit to meet the requirements of a task that involves inquiry, technological problem solving, or decision making. There are four parts to the Unit Task:
  - The Introduction presents the task.
  - The Preparation provides teaching notes for getting students started on the task and involving them in co-creating criteria for the task.
  - The Presentation prepares students for presenting their Unit Task.

- The Evaluation involves students in self- and peer-assessing the Un
  Tasks and presentations using the co-created criteria.
- The Assessment Check provides guiding questions in the text margin to elicit evidence of student learning.

Reproducible Line Masters

Lesson Line Masters

A set of reproducible line masters is included at the end of each unit. These line masters are designed to connect with specific activities in the lessons. They provide opportunities for students to respond, create, record, practise, reflect, and assess. These line masters are referenced in the margin box at the beginning of each lesson and in bold print in the teaching notes of each lesson so that you can easily locate what you need

Generic Line Masters

Generic line masters are also provided. These line masters provide templates that you can use or modify to fit any lesson or unit. These generic line masters are found in the Program Overview beginning on page 73. They include

- Assessment Rubrics for learning contexts and inquiry skills
- Program Masters for the inquiry process and for recording and sorting information

A list of the generic line masters is on page 72 of this overview. Note that these rubrics are also available on the Program Overview CD-ROM in a modifiable format.

Overview of the *Saskatchewan Science 1–2 Curriculum*

The 2011 Saskatchewan Science curriculum for Grades 1 to 5 replaced the 1998 document as part of the planned provincial curriculum review process. The new provincial program of studies is based on the *Pan-Canadian Protocol for Collaboration on School Curriculum Common Framework of Science Learning Outcomes K to 12* (CMEC, 1997). The new science curriculum is guided by three "broad areas of learning" in the core curriculum that aim to (1) foster lifelong learning, (2) create a sense of self, community, and place, and (3) promote engaged citizenship at local and global levels. Moreover, the new program of studies considers these four "cross-curricular competencies": (1) Developing Thinking, (2) Developing Identity and Interdependence, (3) Developing Literacies, and (4) Developing Social Responsibility. The new science curriculum is written to encompass both the "broad areas of learning" and the "cross-curricular competencies" in order to connect them to Saskatchewan's philosophy and goals of education. Indicators that reflect Saskatchewan content; science, technology, society, and environment (STSE); and perspectives of endemic First Nations and Métis voices are some of the ways the new curriculum is tailored for the province. The goal of the renewal process is to update presentation of trends, theories, and ideas in science and technology and, with regard to students, to help foster scientific literacy and promote an understanding of the relationships among science and technology, society, and the environment.

In the new curriculum, the relationships among these goals and expectations is expressed in the Scientific Literacy Framework diagram (on the next page), which shows the four Foundations of Scientific Literacy—Knowledge (including Indigenous Knowledge), Skills, Attitudes, and STSE—acquired through the learning contexts of Scientific Inquiry, Technological Problem Solving, STSE Decision Making, and Cultural Perspectives. The overall aim is for the acquisition of these foundations to produce a scientifically literate student.

The new science curriculum uses the language of outcomes and indicators, which aligns with the first two stages of the Understanding by Design model (Wiggins and McTighe, 2005). **Outcomes** are statements of what students are expected to know and be able to do by the end of a grade in a particular area of study. The outcomes provide direction for assessment and evaluation, and for program, unit, and lesson planning. The outcomes serve as the "desired results" in the first stage of backward design. **Indicators** represent what students need to know and/or be able to do in order to achieve an outcome. They represent the breadth and the depth of learning related to a particular outcome. Indicators serve as examples of the type of evidence that you would accept to determine whether a student has achieved the desired learning results. Building on these two stages, you then move to stage three and plan learning experiences and instructional activities.

Scientific Literacy Framework

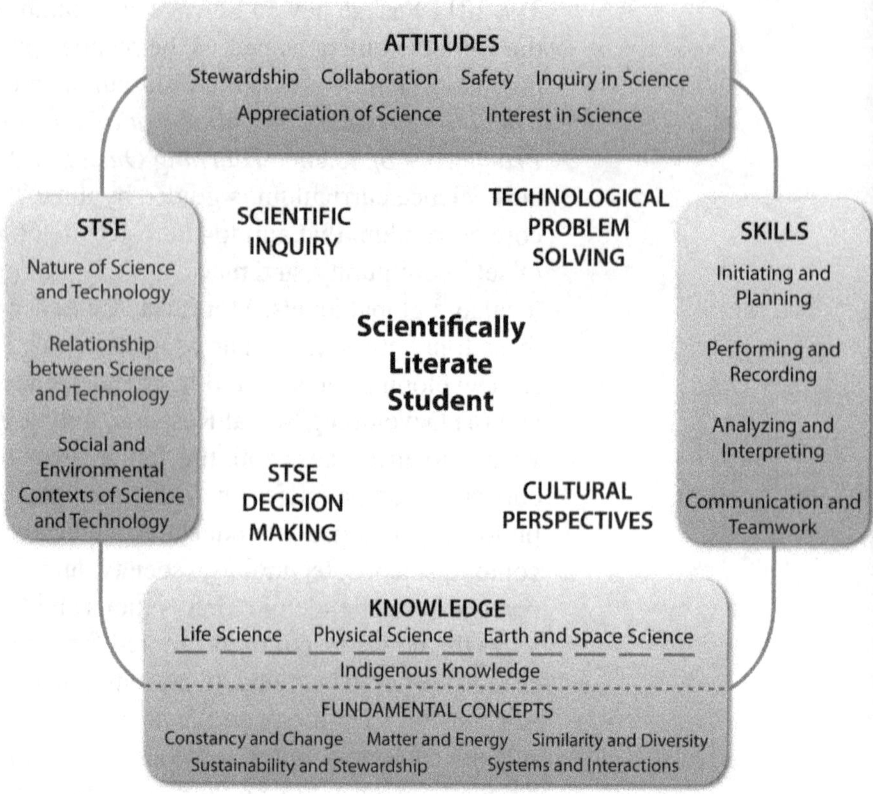

Aims and Goals

The aim of K to 12 science education is to support the development of scientific literacy in all students while considering that scientific literacy today embraces Euro-Canadian and Indigenous heritages. The aim of the Saskatchewan Science curriculum is the development of scientific literacy by all students:

> ***Scientific literacy*** *is an evolving combination of the science-related attitudes, skills, and knowledge students need to develop inquiry, problem-solving, and decision-making abilities to become lifelong learners and to maintain a sense of wonder about the world around them* (p. 4, *Pan-Canadian Protocol for Collaboration on School Curriculum Common Framework of Science Learning Outcomes K to 12* (CMEC, 1997)).

The Ministry of Education has identified four goals for science education. These goals are "*broad statements identifying what students are expected to know and be able to do upon completion of the learning in a particular area of study.*" These goals are written to mirror the foundation statements for scientific literacy identified in the *Common Framework of Science Learning Outcomes K to 12* (CMEC, 1997).

The four goals of K to 12 science are to

- Understand the Nature of Science and STSE Interrelationships: Students will develop an understanding of the nature of science and technology, their interrelationships, and their social and environmental contexts, including interrelationships between the natural and constructed world.
- Construct Scientific Knowledge: Students will construct an understanding of concepts, principles, laws, and theories in life science, physical science, Earth and space science, and Indigenous Knowledge of nature. They will then apply these understandings to interpret, integrate, and extend their knowledge.
- Develop Scientific and Technological Skills: Students will develop the skills required for scientific and technological inquiry, problem solving, and communicating; for working collaboratively; and for making informed decisions.
- Develop Attitudes That Support Scientific Habits of Mind: Students will develop attitudes that support the responsible acquisition and application of scientific, technological, and Indigenous Knowledge to the mutual benefit of self, society, and the environment (*Science 2* (*Saskatchewan Curriculum,* 2011), p. 6).

[NOTE: All references to the Saskatchewan Science curriculum are to *Science 2*. The first section (pages i to 25) of *Science 1* through to *Science 5* is identical in the five grades.]

The main objective of this curriculum, as with many others throughout the world, is to ensure scientific and technological literacy in all students. The *Pearson Science* Program supports the development of scientific and technological literacy in students by providing meaningful contexts, engaging hands-on activities, and student-friendly presentations of basic concepts. *Pearson Science 1 and 2* provide Core Learning Opportunities through Engage, Explore, and Explain activities and a Unit Task that help students meet the learning goals.

The Foundations of Scientific Literacy

The four Foundations of Scientific Literacy are described in the *Common Framework of Science Learning Outcomes K to 12* (CMEC, 1997). These four foundations are interrelated and comprise the critical components of students' scientific literacy.

Foundation 1: Science, Technology, Society, and the Environment (STSE) Interrelationships

The nature of science and technology and their relationships within the social context in which they are developed are explored. Scientific activity and technological processes may be related and may contribute to each other through innovation. They are situated in a social context but they are not dependent on each other.

Nature of Science and Technology

The nature of science and technology as it pertains to the revised curriculum is discussed in the first foundation found in the document *Common Framework of Science Learning Outcomes K to 12* (CMEC, 1997).

Within the Saskatchewan curriculum documents (2011), the following statement is made:

Science is a social and cultural activity anchored in a particular intellectual tradition. ... More than most other ways of knowing nature, science excels at predicting what will happen next, based on its descriptions and explanations of natural and technological phenomena.

Science-based ideas are continually being tested, modified, and improved as new ideas supersede existing ideas. Technology, like science is a creative human activity concerned with solving practical problems that arise from human and social needs, particularly the need to adapt to the environment and to fuel a nation's economy. Research and development lead to new products and processes through the processes of inquiry and design (*Science 2* (*Saskatchewan Curriculum,* 2011), p. 12).

The *Pearson Science* Program presents science and technology as distinct but interdependent disciplines, placing emphasis as appropriate in each unit.

Where the focus of science is on the development and verification of knowledge, in technology the focus is on the development of solutions, involving devices and systems that meet a given need within the constraints of the problem (*Science 2* (*Saskatchewan Curriculum,* 2011), p. 12).

Foundation 2: Scientific Knowledge

The widely accepted disciplines of life science, physical science, and earth and space science, as reflected in the organization of the units, frame the Scientific Knowledge foundation.

A strong science program also recognizes that modern science is not the only way to know nature. A strong science program also includes traditional Indigenous Knowledge. Both scientific knowledge and Indigenous Knowledge are "a cumulative body of knowledge, know-how, practices, and representations developed by people with extended histories of interaction with the natural environment" (*Science 2* (*Saskatchewan Curriculum,* 2011), p. 14).

The *Pearson Science* Program seamlessly integrates scientific and Indigenous Knowledge, where appropriate. To learn more about Indigenous Knowledge, see Section 4 of this Program Overview, Helping Students Relate Science and Technology to the World Outside the School (pp. 50–66).

Fundamental Ideas—Linking Scientific Disciplines

Five fundamental ideas have been identified to help students connect their learning from one science discipline to another and to ground their knowledge in a larger context. These are strands that run throughout a student's science career from K to 12, becoming progressively more elaborate. The ideas are presented in a chart in the Saskatchewan Science curriculum documents (2011, p. 15).

Constancy and Change	The ideas of constancy and change underlie understanding of the natural and constructed world. Through observations, students learn that some characteristics of materials and systems remain constant over time whereas other characteristics change. These changes vary in rate, scale, and pattern, including trends and cycles, and may be quantified using mathematics, particularly measurement.
Matter and Energy	Objects in the physical world are comprised of matter. Students examine materials to understand their properties and structures. The idea of energy provides a conceptual tool that brings together many understandings about natural phenomena, materials, and the process of change. Energy, whether transmitted or transformed, is the driving force of both movement and change.
Similarity and Diversity	The ideas of similarity and diversity provide tools for organizing our experiences with the natural and constructed world. Beginning with informal experiences, students learn to recognize attributes of materials that help to make useful distinctions between one type of material and another, and between one event and another. Over time, students adopt accepted procedures and protocols for describing and classifying objects they encounter, thus enabling them to share ideas with others and to reflect on their own experiences.
Systems and Interactions	An important way to understand and interpret the world is to think about the whole in terms of its parts and alternately about its parts in terms of how they relate to one another and to the whole. A system is an organized group of related objects or components that interact with one another so that the overall effect is much greater than that of the individual parts, even when these are considered together.
Sustainability and Stewardship	Sustainability refers to the ability to meet our present needs without compromising the ability of future generations to meet their needs. Stewardship refers to the personal responsibility to take action in order to participate in the responsible management of natural resources. By developing their understanding of ideas related to sustainability, students are able to take increasing responsibility for making choices that reflect those ideas.

Foundation 3: Scientific and Technological Skills and Processes

Answering questions, solving problems, and making decisions challenge students to develop the skills of initiating and planning, performing and recording, and analyzing and interpreting in an atmosphere that requires communication and teamwork. The *Pearson Science* Program provides challenges of increasing scope and complexity as students progress through Grades 1 and 2.

Focus on Skills

Teachers are encouraged to promote student achievement by providing students with opportunities to practise skills. The Saskatchewan Science curriculum encourages teachers to provide experiences that challenge students. Through classroom investigations and science challenges, skills such as initiating and planning, performing and recording, and analyzing and interpreting are engaged. Skills of communication and teamwork essential to the development and application of ideas are fostered.

Foundation 4: Attitudes

Students are encouraged to develop attitudes, values, and ethics for the responsible use of science and technology. Development of scientific literacy will be supported by the following attitudes:

- appreciation of the contributions and the limitations of science and technology
- interest in science at home, at school, and in the community
- understanding the need for evidence and reasoned argument in the development of scientific knowledge
- appreciation of competence in collaboration with others
- awareness of the responsibility for stewardship in society and the environment
- concern for safety when engaged in scientific or technological activity

Focus on Assessment and Evaluation of Student Achievement

As stated on page 35 of *Science 2* (*Saskatchewan Curriculum,* 2011), "*All assessment and evaluation of student achievement must be based on the outcomes in the provincial curriculum.*" Three types of assessment contribute to the overall picture of student achievement.

Assessment ***for*** learning is ongoing through the teaching and learning process and provides information to help students improve their learning. Differentiated instruction may be involved to ensure support of different modes of student learning.

Assessment ***as*** learning occurs throughout the learning process and involves students' reflection on their own progress in relation to learning associated with curricular outcomes.

Assessment ***of*** learning occurs at the end of a learning cycle and uses evidence of student achievement of curricular outcomes.

Connections with Other Areas of Study

Deeper understanding of some learning outcomes may be obtained through integration of disciplines. Some outcomes allow for subject-area integration. An integrated approach must help student learning of the related disciplines and understanding of the conceptual connections. Both of the subject areas' outcomes must be achieved and in-depth learning must occur. Be cautious not to lose the integrity of any of the subjects.

Examples of subject-area integration are included in the Science curriculum documents (*Saskatchewan Curriculum*, 2011) on pages 37 to 39. The *Pearson Science 1 and 2 Teacher's Resources* also provide a list of specific indicators from other disciplines that might be met during each lesson.

References

Council of Ministers of Education, Canada. (1997). *Common framework of science learning outcomes: Pan-Canadian protocol for collaboration on school curriculum, K–12*. Ontario: Council of Ministers of Education.

Saskatchewan Ministry of Education. (2011). *Science 2.* Saskatchewan Ministry of Education. Available at http://www.education.gov.sk.ca/science-curricula

Working with Groups

The *Pearson Science* Program provides a balance of whole-class, small-group, partner, and individual learning opportunities for students to investigate questions, solve problems, take risks, compare results, analyze their findings, and take responsibility for their own learning. Ample opportunity is given for the development of the attitudes described in the fourth foundation of scientific literacy on page 12 of this document.

Whole Class: In *Pearson Science 1 and 2*, the Engage section of most lessons in each unit uses large-group instruction to introduce new topics and concepts. Throughout the lessons in each unit, there are opportunities in Explore and Explain activities to discuss, explore, investigate, read aloud, synthesize, and clarify understanding with the class as a whole.

Partner and Small Group: Many of the activities found in the Explore and Explain sections of the lessons in *Pearson Science 1 and 2* suggest that students work in pairs or small groups. These groupings allow students to develop ideas and solutions to problems that they might not consider if they were working in isolation. In addition, group activities provide students with opportunities to

- share their ideas readily
- work co-operatively
- learn from one another
- appreciate the capabilities of others
- become more responsible for their own learning
- develop leadership and communication skills

Forming heterogeneous groups based on a range of student abilities will provide opportunities for weaker students to learn from stronger students. This will also help the class develop an appreciation of one another's talents and expertise.

To ensure successful group work and develop students' co-operative work skills, you may like to assign a group role, such as Recorder, Materials Manager, and Communicator, to each student in the group. Ensure that you rotate roles among students and provide opportunities for students to experience each role.

Some group activities require closer supervision than others. One option is to involve adult volunteers or to pair each group with a student from a higher grade who is familiar with the tools and materials and who will act as a peer tutor. Another option is to supervise the work of one small group at a time while the rest of the class works on a different activity that requires less supervision.

Individual: The Explain section of the lessons in *Pearson Science 1 and 2* provides many opportunities for individual work. The activities in this section allow students to integrate new knowledge through quiet reflection, to demonstrate their abilities and knowledge, and to incorporate their own interests.

Equipment and Materials

Obtaining Materials

You can find many of the materials you need for a successful science program at school (such as paper clips, glue sticks, and cardboard) and at home (such as balloons, nails, magazines, and cooking oil). Before you begin a new unit, check the lists of required materials for the activities and send a letter home with students requesting donations of materials.

Local businesses can also be useful sources of materials. Often, they are willing to provide the neighbourhood school with classroom materials. A building contractor might be able to supply pieces of wood, and the local department store may donate empty shoe boxes. School science supply companies are another source. They sell more specialized items such as thermometers, magnifying glasses, and droppers.

Storing Materials

Open shelves and plastic bins are invaluable for organizing required materials and equipment. Label the shelves and bins to keep things orderly and encourage students to put objects back in their proper places.

There are two approaches to organizing classroom materials and equipment. The first promotes student independence and responsibility. All materials and equipment are stored on labelled shelves and in bins accessible to students. When the class works on an activity, each group or pair of students is responsible for collecting the materials they need and for returning the materials to their appropriate places when they are finished. You will probably find that this approach requires a few extra minutes of class time for students to collect and return the materials.

The second approach saves on class time but requires more teacher preparation. All materials and equipment necessary for an activity or experiment are placed in labelled bins and distributed to groups or pairs of students and then collected at the end of the period. A checklist of the bin items is included with each bin, and students are responsible for checking that all items are returned to the bins.

Use of Digital Technology in the Classroom

Digital technology is now so pervasive in everyday life that you may find it useful in the classroom. You may wish to use

- in-class devices such as interactive whiteboards, which can be used for reviewing information through interactive multiple-choice games
- a multimedia projector that is connected to an in-class computer, which will allow you to project computer images, websites, and videos
- flip cameras or smart devices, which are easy for students to use to record in-class videos as suggested in the Observing and Recording skills poster
- in-class or in-school computers so that all students can access information online. Compile website addresses in a folder on a shared drive so that students can "click and go" to websites that you have previewed. Model how to identify and use key words as search terms for websites, images, and videos.

Be aware of the need for supervision and provision of adequate safeguards to prevent exploitation of students through Internet access.

Constructivism in the Science Classroom

The Construction of Knowledge

Halfway through a first-period Monday morning science class, a teacher and her class were surprised when a bat began to fly around their classroom. The bat, which had managed to get into the school over the weekend, had been roosting quietly on the ceiling when it was startled by student voices. Science that day became a lesson in how well bats can fly in a classroom as the teacher struggled to capture the bat. Over the next few days, the teacher was able to draw on the flood of questions about bats to continue with the unit on sound, illustrating points by using the example of how bats navigate during flight by echolocation.

Science teachers often capitalize on such experiences to help students understand science concepts. Newspaper articles, popular television shows, features in science magazines, and local events routinely become part of science lessons as teachers build on existing student interests to make science a motivating and relevant subject.

Less common are attempts by teachers to discover the prior experiences and beliefs that students bring to science classrooms and how these experiences relate to the students' ability to learn science concepts. Over the past four decades, research in science education has clearly shown that every student has a unique mind that is constantly engaged in the construction of understanding as he or she makes sense of new ideas within the framework of pre-existing beliefs and ideas. How students make sense of the new ideas presented in science classes clearly depends on their life experiences and a myriad of complex factors such as the students' family situation, religious beliefs, or gender. These factors result in a unique and dynamic framework of thinking for each student that affects how the student comes to understand scientific concepts.

What Is Constructivism?

The belief that students actively construct new knowledge and understanding based on their pre-existing patterns of thinking and beliefs is called *constructivism* (or *constructivist learning theory*). Most science teachers incorporate some aspects of constructivist learning theory in their practice, especially when they link science concepts to students' prior learning when introducing a new idea. For example, a teacher beginning a unit on exploring animal growth and changes might ask students to share their experiences with animals as they grow from babies to adults; if beginning a unit on daily and seasonal change, a teacher might ask students to relate what they do differently from day to night and from season to season. Even though each student has a unique frame of understanding, most science teachers assume that students have enough common experiences to provide the conceptual links for science concepts to be learned accurately and well.

Research suggests, however, that teachers should question this assumption. In some cases, students' individual prior understandings or preconceptions complement what is taught in science classrooms, leading to a deeper understanding of the science topic. It is much more common, however, that students' existing ideas and beliefs vary considerably and that these prior understandings compete with what they are taught. The result is often a confusing blend of ideas or the outright refusal by students to believe the ideas presented in their science classes. This was demonstrated by a group of pre-service science teachers who, prior to an activity, argued that the heavier an object, the faster it will fall. Every one of these university students had successfully completed senior courses in secondary school physics and claimed to have learned well the principles and calculations for objects in free fall. Only when they dropped similar balls of very different densities at the same time did these university students finally come to change their beliefs, often with gasps of total amazement.

Research into how students construct beliefs and ideas reveals that, once in place, a preconception is very resilient. Studies on the development of students' concepts have discovered that usual practices of science education can make preconceptions worse. A good example is a study that found Grade 3 children understand that when water evaporates, the water turns into "tiny particles" that exist in the air. Students in junior high school, however, were more likely to explain that, through evaporation, the water turns into oxygen and hydrogen gas! Researchers discovered that, over time, students accommodated their prior beliefs about evaporation by blending new scientific terminology with their prior knowledge, creating a misconception. In other words, students learned very well how to make "scientific noises," which then led to the development of the misconception. Most disturbing of all is that decades of research on how students learn science concepts reveals that students hold misconceptions about practically every science topic in the school curriculum, and that these views interfere with the ability of students to learn science.

Being a Constructivist Teacher

Constructivist learning theory uses such research to develop teaching practices in science education that ensure students learn science concepts accurately. This approach not only exposes and deals with students' preconceptions but also provides a pedagogy that more accurately reflects how scientists work while opening the world of science to students' experiences and backgrounds. In this way, constructivism in science education helps students acquire the scientific literacy needed to be informed, active citizens in today's changing world by developing a critical understanding of the world of science and by ensuring students learn science concepts well.

Since most people learn best through experience, constructivism argues that it is important for teachers to adapt their approaches to match how students learn by adopting a highly experiential, hands-on teaching methodology. Most successful science teachers incorporate hands-on activities when teaching science concepts. Typically, these activities, or "labs," follow teacher-led introductions to the science topic. Constructivist learning theory argues that this approach is at odds with how most people learn, suggesting that teachers should begin their science classes with concrete, hands-on experiences, and from these experiences begin to develop science concepts with students actively involved in the development process. For example, teachers might begin physics lesson on free fall by challenging students to find a rule about how objects fall. From student experiences of dropping objects, the science class can then lead to a discussion that will reveal that the mass of an object does not affect the rate of fall. In this way, the lesson moves from a concrete experience to the abstract concept, not the reverse.

There are many reasons to begin teaching a science concept with experiences that lead to concept development.

- First, preliminary explorations through experience will help you gauge the extent to which students already understand the science concept.
- Second, teachers who explore student understanding through hands-on activities are given a valuable opportunity to uncover misconceptions. Once you have identified these misconceptions, you can modify your lesson plans to include activities that directly challenge students' prior beliefs.
- Third, beginning science education with hands-on experiences helps develop students into a community of scientists. Science thus becomes an invitation to exploration where knowledge co-emerges through interactions among students, the teacher, and other resources. In this way, the authority for knowledge development shifts from you to a group process that more accurately reflects how scientists work.
- Finally, the discussion that follows the experience allows students to contribute insights that may be overlooked in a lesson that begins with an abstract idea. For example, a class discussion of what students observed through their examination of living things could provide an opportunity to enrich science education as students share viewpoints from their various cultural backgrounds on the classification of living things.

"Hands On, Minds On"

Constructivism is not discovery learning. Students seldom "discover" scientific concepts independently through hands-on investigation; rather, new concepts must be presented when students are in a receptive state. Often, this is when they have been confronted with the inadequacy of their views in explaining an observation they have made in an activity. The classroom discussions with you and classmates should guide students in assimilating hands-on experiences and integrating them into new concepts. This method is sometimes called "hands on, minds on," to emphasize the importance of restructuring students' preconceptions through both discussion and hands-on investigation.

Most adults retain at least some preconceptions about scientific concepts. Be aware that such ideas can restrict further understanding of science both for you and for the student, and try to identify and challenge your own misconceptions. Finally, note that computer-based simulations are becoming more available. These will help to challenge students' preconceptions by providing a visual approach to concepts that previously could only be presented theoretically. Take full advantage of these aids as they become available for your classroom.

Incorporating Language and Literacy into a Science Program

Literacy—The Reading and Writing Connection

Reading and writing are intricately connected. When readers and writers share the same understanding of how a text is constructed, they are able to communicate easily. The many decisions a writer makes in terms of audience, topic, and format will contribute to how well readers are able to understand the text. Readers who understand the writer's decision-making process and who can recognize the organizational patterns used are able to focus their attention more on the meaning of what they are reading.

Connecting Reading and Writing in the *Pearson Science* Program

Pearson Education believes it is essential to integrate language and literacy instruction in all subject areas in Grades 1 and 2. These years provide the essential building blocks in the development of students' language and literacy skills. The main focus of the *Pearson Science Grades 1 and 2* resources is to provide a program that meets the outcomes and indicators of the science curriculum while acknowledging the importance of the development of literacy (reading, viewing, listening, writing, and speaking) in these grades. The fiction and non-fiction Little Books are intended to address the science curriculum; however, the Little Books can also be used to supplement your literacy program. Level I of Fountas and Pinnell was used as a guide for writing the books. With instruction and guidance, students reading at different levels will be able to access the text supported by illustrations, photos, and charts.

The *Pearson Science 1 and 2 Teacher's Resources* provide literacy strategies (Before, During, and After) for guiding reading in small groups with the Little Books, as well as shared reading with the Lap Books. Along with the Science Indicators, the Assessment Chart in each lesson identifies some of the English Language Arts indicators addressed by the activities. Because Grades 1 and 2 are foundational years in the development of students' language and literacy skills, *Pearson Science 1 and 2* supports this integrated approach to learning.

The content of science is used to

- emphasize the importance of language use from a holistic perspective
- encourage small-group discussion, emphasizing listening and speaking skills
- develop the use of cueing systems in reading and writing
- develop students' reading skills using the fiction and non-fiction Little Books
- develop the use of before, during, and after strategies in each of the strands of reading, writing, speaking, listening, viewing, and representing

- expand students' active vocabulary
- highlight important language patterns
- support or "scaffold" students' writing, including recording observations and sharing the results of investigations

How to Develop Students' Reading Skills

To help students get the most out of the fiction and non-fiction Little Books, you may wish to provide guidance and direction so students can gain information from texts that are beyond their independent reading level, and develop a repertoire of strategic reading skills. With frequent practice, students internalize strategies that help them become more independent readers of difficult material. Many students benefit from this kind of support throughout elementary school and beyond.

Three stages in a guided, or directed, reading process are outlined below. The activities and strategies in each stage can also be used in a shared reading process (see page 24). These strategies may also apply when students are listening or viewing material.

Before Reading

Use some of the following activities to prepare students for the material they are going to read.

- **Activate and build prior knowledge and experience.** Elicit what students already know about the topic. Provide an opportunity for them to share related experiences. Guide students to make predictions based on their background knowledge and experience.
- **Have students preview the text using a guided Picture Walk.** Begin by discussing the title and the cover illustration and making predictions about the content of the book. Then, move on to examine each two-page spread. Encourage students to share their observations about what they see in the illustrations and to make predictions about the content and the words they might see in the text. A related strategy is **View, Pause, Predict, and Think Aloud**. Ask students to look at the pictures, pause to think about what they see, and then take turns thinking aloud to predict what some of the words on the spread might be.
- **Set the stage and prepare students conceptually** for the material they are going to read. Use the **Unit Opener** and the **Engage** and **Explore** activities suggested for each lesson to develop the conceptual understanding that will facilitate students' success with the Little Books.
- **Pre-teach key words** that will enhance students' comprehension of the text. A related strategy is **List, Group, and Label**. List as many words as students can think of that relate to the topic. Write the words on sticky notes or index cards. Then, ask students which words might go together. Have students work in small groups or as a class to group the words on large sheets of chart paper. Then, challenge students to suggest titles or labels for each group.

- **Encourage students to ask questions and/or make "I wonder ..." statements** about the topic of the Little Books.
- **Set a purpose for reading.** Discuss with students whether they are reading to find out what happens (fiction), or reading to find out more about a topic (non-fiction). Ask students to think about why they are reading the text.
- **Think about the author's purpose for writing this text.** Discuss with students whether they think the author wrote this text to provide information or to tell a story. Identify textual clues that support their decision.
- Use the **Preview, Connect, and Predict strategy**. Have students preview pages, make connections to activities they have done or experiences they have had, and make predictions about the text.
- **Preview pages of non-fiction text for features** such as titles, captions headings, diagrams, and labels, and discuss their purpose.

During Reading

Use the following strategies.

- "Chunk" the text into manageable sections. The information in the Little Books is organized in two-page spreads. Focus on one spread at a time.
- Provide a pre-reading question related to the main idea of each chunk of text.
- **Discuss the illustrations on each spread** to provide a context for the written text. Use the illustrations to ask questions related to the written text.
- **Confirm students' predictions, make new predictions, or adjust previous predictions** as you move from one two-page spread to the next.
- Read aloud the text in the fiction and non-fiction Little Books and have students follow along in their books. Developing readers may need to finger-point or use a ruler or bookmark to guide their eyes along the lines of text. Encourage those students who are able to join in with you as you read. Reading the text aloud as students follow also provides an opportunity to model how to deal with new words. Use a Think Aloud strategy to model how to use picture clues to help decode text, how to chunk longer or more difficult words into smaller parts, and how to use context and background knowledge to infer the meaning of new words.
- **Pause to visualize the content and/or predictions.** Guide students to construct mental images of the action/content. Provide opportunities for students to share what they picture and/or see, hear, smell, feel, and taste in their minds.
- **Use clues from the illustrations and the context of the written text to identify unknown words.** Guide students to use what they know about the content of the book, what they know about words, and what they can see in the illustrations on each spread to identify new or difficult words. Students could skip the word, read or listen to the end

of the sentence, and then go back to see if they can figure out what the word means from the context.

- **Make connections between the text and students' experiences and background knowledge.** Provide opportunities for students to construct deeper meaning from the text by sharing what the text reminds them of or what they have experienced that is similar.
- Stop after each two-page spread to check that students can identify the main idea or can answer the pre-reading question. Answer students' questions before moving on to the next section of text.
- **Encourage students to ask questions about the content** as you read. Invite them to share what they wonder about or what confuses them.
- **Practise using cueing systems to construct meaning.** This includes *textual cues* that tell whether it is fiction or non-fiction and what text form it is; *pragmatic cues* that tell who the intended audience is and the author's purpose in writing the text; *semantic cues* that tell what new words mean; *syntactic cues* that tell how language is written correctly, including sentence structure and word order; *graphophonic cues* that connect sounds and symbols; and *other cues*, including features such as graphs, charts, and visuals, that authors use to help us understand the text.

After Reading

Use some of the following strategies to help students review and revisit what they just read.

- **Recall the key ideas from the text.** Have students share what they learned from reading the text. For the fiction Little Books, have students participate in retelling the events of the story and then sequencing them in the correct order.
- **Identify what students learned from the text** and encourage them to ask further questions based on what they learned. You may want to have them summarize the main ideas or look or listen for a single sentence or image that conveys the main point of a chunk of text.
- **Invite students to evaluate what they read.** What did they like/dislike about the text? What made the text a success? How could the text have been better? What would they add or take away to make the text better?
- **Highlight key words and new vocabulary**, and review the cues that will help students remember them. Invite students to share words or language from the text that they particularly liked or remember clearly.
- **Provide an opportunity for students to respond personally to the text** by sharing what it makes them think of, what it reminds them of, or a similar story or book they have heard or read.
- **Deepen their understanding and enjoyment by rereading the text, creating a representation, or by further discussion, dramatization, or role playing.**

Shared Reading

This approach to reading with students involves reading from a Big Book with enlarged print and illustrations so students can see the text, or providing students with copies of the same text that you are reading. During this process, it is essential that students see the same text that you are reading. On the first reading, you may wish to read the text without stopping so students can listen to and enjoy the story, or you may wish to pause at appropriate points to provide an opportunity for students to make predictions. If reading from a Big Book, you may wish to move a pointer or your finger under the text to reinforce sound-symbol correspondence on the first reading or on subsequent readings. As you reread the text, pause at appropriate points to allow students to predict what the next word is or to chant repeated text. This is sometimes called fill-in-the-gap reading because you read most of the text but you pause for students to chime in with rhyming words or other predictable words in the text. Encourage students to join in with the oral reading as they feel comfortable and more confident about the text. The point is that you provide an opportunity for students to experience the same text over several readings. With each reading, they are able to become more involved as they become familiar with the vocabulary and the features of the text. When students are familiar with the story or the content, you can focus more on the text. You might mask key words so students have to provide words that would fit the context of sentences. You might go on word hunts to look for high-frequency words, key content words, rhyming words, words with a certain number of beats or syllables, and so on.

You can also use echo reading and choral reading. In echo reading, students echo, or reread, the words you read to them. In choral reading, students read with you. When students are familiar with a text, you can also identify parts in the text or roles in the story and then group students so that each group reads one part of the text or role in the story. Choral reading can become choral dramatic reading.

How to Develop Students' Writing Skills

Shared writing can be used to model the process of recording oral language and the development of different forms of writing. During shared writing, you and your students compose written text together, while you act as the recorder. Shared writing allows you to engage students in the processes of writing, provide instruction about how a particular text should be written, and model the thought processes that students will need to use in their independent writing. Use shared writing as an opportunity to model the continuous cycle of revisions that writers use to create stronger, more powerful written text. Involve students in rereading the written text you have composed together. Because the text uses shared language, it provides an authentic opportunity to practise and reinforce reading skills.

Note that many of the strategies on the following pages can also be applied to speaking and creating.

Before Writing

Provide guidance and modelling in the use of the following strategies.

- **Activate prior/background knowledge.** Discuss with students what they already know about a topic and consider what message needs to be shared or what questions need to be answered in the written text.
- **Identify the role or point of view of the writer.** Decide if we are writing as a character or as the narrator (or storyteller).
- **Identify our purpose in writing.** Is it to share what we know? Is it to write a story? Is it to record what we found out?
- **Decide on the best form for achieving the writing purpose.** Involving students in connecting form and purpose will help them make more informed decisions as they begin to do more independent writing.
- **Brainstorm for ideas and information.** This can be a way to activate prior knowledge and assess what students know.
- **Consider whether more information is needed.** If so, discuss how students can learn what they need to know—who to ask, where to look, how to find out.
- **Plan and organize ideas for writing.** Consider the recorded ideas and information. Do we need to put them in order when we write so that our ideas and information make sense? If so, how will we arrange them so they make sense? How will we begin writing? How will we end our writing?

During Writing

Provide guidance and modelling in the use of the following strategies.

- **Create the first draft on the whiteboard or chart paper.** Guide students to contribute ideas and suggestions orally, and model how the spoken word can be written.
- **Reread written text to check and correct.** After each sentence or group of ideas is recorded, model how to reread the text to make sure it makes sense, says what students want it to say, and uses words correctly. Show students how to add words and make changes and corrections to the text. Ask them to think about whether they can use more interesting words. Invite students to join in the rereading if they are able to reinforce the connection between writing and reading.
- **Experiment with different ways to communicate ideas and information clearly and effectively.** Try different formats and ways of expressing ideas and information to see which ones students think work best. This models the process they will need to use when they write independently.
- **Reflect on purpose and form.** As you are writing with students, pause periodically to compare what is being written with the purpose for writing. Do students' written ideas meet the chosen purpose? Also, consider whether the written text matches the chosen form.

- **Use punctuation to signal readers how to read what is written.** Explain that punctuation marks tell readers where to pause for a breath They add meaning to the text because they tell readers how the writer wants the text to be read. Involve students in deciding which punctuation marks should be used to match the meaning they want (e.g., dialogue in fiction, asking questions, stating information).
- **Involve students in applying what they know about sound-symbol connections to help spell words.**

After Writing

As you model the rereading or involve students in rereading chorally with you, provide guidance and modelling in the use of the following strategies.

- **Reread to check for content and meaning.** Ask students to listen and watch for whether the text says everything they need it to say. Does the text meet the chosen purpose? Are there ideas that need to be changed, added, or deleted?
- **Reread to check for organization.** Ask students to listen and watch for the order of ideas and information. Does the order make sense? Do any ideas or details need to be re-ordered?
- **Reread for sentence structure and word choice.** Ask students to listen and watch for complete thoughts and places where they could use more interesting or better words. Are they using any words too many times? Have any words been left out? Did they use the correct words, especially the science content words?
- **Check for correct use of capital letters and punctuation.**

How to Encourage Group Discussion

All students need many opportunities to explore ideas and clarify information through group discussion. Group work is especially beneficial for EAL/ELL students, who need many opportunities to speak English but may feel shy or anxious about doing so in front of the whole class. However, effective group work may not happen unless you use specific strategies, such as the following, to ensure that all students are actively involved.

- **Generate ideas through small-group brainstorming.** Group brainstorming gives all students an opportunity to take risks in a way that they may be reluctant to take in front of the class. It is useful as an introductory activity or a pre-reading strategy to activate prior knowledge and generate questions.
- **Think–Pair–Share** provides an opportunity for students to think about a key question or prompt on their own before any sharing is done. During this time, they might record their thoughts as written text or as illustrations. After individual thinking time, give students an opportunity to share their thoughts with a partner and to compile a response to the question or prompt. Then, give each pair an opportunity to share their combined response or ideas with another pair or with the class.

- **Help students review, internalize, or apply new concepts and information through group rehearsal.** For example, after a classroom presentation of new material, pose a review or extension question to the whole class. Instead of asking for volunteers to answer the question, instruct students to discuss the question in small groups. Inform the class that you will select, at random, an individual from a group to answer the question.
- **Organize "jigsaw" activities and projects** to encourage students to take responsibility for specific tasks and to value each other's contributions. In a "jigsaw" activity, students are placed in groups, and each group discusses, explores, or investigates a different topic (or aspect of a topic). Then, students are regrouped so that an "expert" on each topic (or aspect of the topic) is included in each new group. Each "expert" has a piece of the total learning puzzle and shares his or her information with his or her group members.
- **Teach group skills and language**. Group work provides an ideal opportunity for helping all students develop a repertoire of collaborative skills such as taking turns, staying on task, seeking consensus, and managing controversy and disagreement. Many of these skills involve the use of specific language expressions, some of which need to be explicitly taught, especially when there are second-language learners in the class. Provide opportunities for students to talk about the language they can use to improve the group process. For example, say something like "I noticed that not everybody was taking turns in the conversation, and some people were getting more than their fair share of turns to talk. I wonder what we can say when we want to take a turn, or we want to offer a turn to someone who may be rather shy? What can we say if someone is speaking too much? How can we help the students who are just learning English?" You may wish to use the Science Skills Poster: Communicating and Teamwork to introduce or review important aspects of group work.

Differentiated Instruction
by Karen Hume

What Is Differentiated Instruction?

There is no need to differentiate all day, every day.
– Karen Hume

Differentiated instruction is instruction that has a significant, positive impact on student achievement and involves the teacher making small alterations to successful, effective practices in order to respond to an individual's readiness, interests, or learning preferences.

Differentiation is an organizing framework for everything that happens in teaching and learning. The first half of the definition refers to instruction that is, first of all, effective—that has a significant, positive impact on student achievement. The second half of the definition refers to instruction that is responsive—that makes small alterations to successful, effective practices in order to respond to an individual's readiness, interests, or learning preferences.

Let's look at each part of the definition in turn. To ensure effective instruction, teachers plan using the model of backward design developed by Grant Wiggins and Jay McTighe. This model has three steps:

1. Identify the learning intentions of the unit in some detail and frame those intentions in the form of big ideas and essential questions so that students are involved in inquiry.
2. Determine the assessments *for*, *as*, and *of* learning that will be used at all stages of the learning to determine what students know, understand, and are able to do. Assessments *for* and *as* learning are used to determine next steps in instruction. Assessments *of* learning evaluate student understanding and skill.
3. Plan activities that are aligned with the learning intentions and assessments. Activities are based on powerful instructional strategies, such as the list generated by Robert Marzano's review of the last 35 years of educational research, and may be differentiated as needed or desired. Strategies are taught and assessed in the context of a strong learning community, one in which students are aware of their own strengths and needs, and supportive of the strengths and needs of others.

Differentiation applies to students in all classes and to students with special needs, learners of English as an additional language, and gifted students. Learning happens only when teachers "start where they are" (Hume, 2008), meaning that teachers build on students' prior knowledge and link to their readiness, interests, or learning preferences.

To ensure responsive instruction, teachers are aware of the readiness, interests, and learning preferences of the learner and offer the appropriate degree of challenge to significantly increase both student engagement and academic success.

1. Readiness

What Is It?

Students are at different points of readiness for learning different concepts based on their background knowledge of those concepts. Think of readiness as being on a continuum with three points:

Emerging ←——→ On Track ←——→ Advanced

Why Is It Important?

Readiness is a more positive and useful term than *ability*. All learners are at different points of readiness for different concepts, depending on their background knowledge; no learner is a struggling student all of the time.

How Do Teachers Determine a Student's Readiness?

Readiness can be determined only through assessments for learning. Teachers should ensure that pre-assessments and formative assessments are targeted to address exactly what they need to know about student understanding of key concepts. If teachers use the Unit Openers to make students aware of the skills they will use and the concepts they will learn over the course of the unit, they can help students see their growth in understanding from "emerging" to "on track" or "advanced."

How to Support Different Points of Readiness

- Create tiered assignments. Tiered assignments provide different levels of the same activity to meet the differing stages of readiness for the concept you are teaching. The easiest way to create a tiered assignment is to either begin with or create an activity for "on track" students and then modify it by varying in either direction according to one or more of the considerations in the following chart:

	Emerging Readiness	**On Track**	**Advanced Readiness**
Concepts	Concrete	Mostly concrete, with some abstraction	Abstract
Procedure	Minimal number of steps to complete the assignment	Can require more steps to complete the assignment	Can be more open-ended, leaving decisions about how the assignment is completed to the student
Reading Level	Appropriate to participants; may be below grade level	At grade level	Above grade level
Teacher Support	Teacher may model or partially complete the activity to provide examples.	Teacher provides some verbal or written support.	Teacher provides support as needed.

- Use short-term flexible learning groups. Teachers may physically group students or just mentally group students according to the assignment, choosing homogeneous groupings based on readiness or heterogeneous groupings in which students at different readiness point work together.

2. Interest

Why Is It Important?

Engagement and expertise go hand in hand with students' areas of interest. Since students' interests influence their background knowledge, and since learning happens only when building on prior understanding, knowing students' areas of interest helps teachers to make relevant connections to support those who are at an emerging point of readiness for a key concept.

How Do Teachers Determine Students' Interests?

Casual conversations are the fastest and easiest way to determine students' interests.

How to Support Students' Interests

- Use knowledge of students' interests to provide relevant connections when a student is struggling with a key concept.
- Provide students with exit cards at the end of class. An exit card is an index card on which students respond to a prompt. For example, you might ask students to talk or write about the similarities and differences between the day's lesson and an area of interest.

3. Learning Preferences

What Are They?

There are two categories of learning preferences that are often considered in the differentiated classroom:

- Learning styles refer to the ways an individual acquires and processes information. The most commonly referenced learning styles are represented by the acronym VAK—visual, auditory, and kinesthetic.
- Intelligence preferences refer to the ways in which an individual naturally tends to work when confronted with a difficult problem or when creating something new. Howard Gardner's multiple intelligences are one grouping of intelligence preferences; Robert Sternberg's triarchic intelligences are another.

Why Are They Important?

Since learning preferences refer to the natural ways in which we learn, students have an easier time learning new concepts when they are allowed to work according to their preferences.

How Do Teachers Determine a Student's Learning Preferences?

Use inventories (Hume, 2008) or provide learning stations that allow students to learn or practise a concept in a variety of forms. Observe their responses.

How to Support Student Learning Preferences

- Teach the whole class a single concept in a variety of forms. Fortunately, science teachers have a wonderful advantage in being able to offer plenty of opportunities for kinesthetic activity through science experiments.
- Allow students to sometimes choose their preferred way of working. A good rule of thumb is to allow students to work according to their strengths when a concept is challenging, and to push students to work in areas that aren't strengths when a concept is easy.

Differentiation is based on teachers knowing their learners, but you do not need to know everything about each of the many students you teach. There is also no need to differentiate all day, every day. Rather, you can use your understanding of students' readiness, interests, or learning preferences and your knowledge of the curriculum to tweak currently successful practices around key concepts so you will reach a few more learners.

For further information and lots of practical suggestions about how to differentiate instruction, refer to

Hume, Karen. (2008). *Start where they are: Differentiating for success with the young adolescent*. Toronto: Pearson Canada. (includes 88 modifiable line masters)

Ontario Ministry of Education. (2007). *Differentiated instruction educator's package*. Toronto: Student Success Training, Implementation and Evaluation Branch.

References

Gardner, Howard. (2006). *Multiple intelligences: New horizons.* New York: Basic Books.

Marzano, Robert. (2003). *What works in schools: Translating research into action.* Virginia: ASCD.

Sternberg, Robert. (1996). *Successful intelligence.* New York: Simon & Schuster.

2 Assessment and Evaluation

Planning for Assessment

Clear Targets and Criteria for Success

The aim of K to 12 science education is to support development of scientific literacy in all students while considering that scientific literacy today embraces Euro-Canadian and Indigenous heritages. Specific goals within this aim identify what students are expected to know and be able to do upon completion of study in a particular area.

The goals for students in K to 12 science are to

- understand the nature of science and STSE interrelationships
- construct scientific knowledge
- develop scientific and technological skills
- develop attitudes that support scientific habits of mind

Student assessment is one of the most important tasks in the teaching-learning process, and when considering assessment and evaluation you must think in terms of the goals for students. Assessment advocate Rick Stiggins asserts that "Students can hit any target they can see that holds still for them." Students need to begin their learning journey with the end in mind. In *Pearson Science 1–2,* the big ideas/essential questions of science that are to be covered are listed as key "I wonder …" statements in the Unit Opener.

Research indicates that when students see themselves in the curriculum, they experience greater success. The *Pearson Science* Program relates the content to students' lives through thoughtful planning of activities and use of program resources that build on the background knowledge and experiences of students.

Effective teachers incorporate assessment strategies into all aspects of their teaching; students who know how the assessment process works and who feel their input is valued usually have a greater sense of ownership in their learning. Sharing assessment criteria with students helps them identify what constitutes a range of performances and is a vital step in the assessment process. Rubrics or scoring guides should also be given to students prior to the assessment. Involving students in the development of rubrics is extremely desirable, and the inclusion of editable rubrics should further help to support this.

Examining anchor text of student work helps students better understand criteria, and providing them with examples that demonstrate a range of performances (e.g., Levels 1, 2, 3, and 4) rather than a single example is indeed beneficial. This not only promotes clarity on what a particular performance looks like, but also helps students differentiate between the levels of performance, an important Assessment *as* Learning skill. Student examples shared with students should not have student names on them.

Eight rubrics have been developed specifically to support the key features of the Saskatchewan Science curriculum. These include rubrics for the four Learning Contexts (Scientific Inquiry, Technological Problem Solving, Cultural Perspectives, and STSE Decision Making), which represent different methods of engaging students' inquiry in science. Each rubric addresses aspects of the four Foundations of Scientific Literacy (Knowledge, Skills, STSE, and Attitudes). You may use these rubrics to assess student learning of the outcomes in a particular unit or part of a unit.

The other four rubrics assess the four Skills of Scientific Literacy (Initiating and Planning, Performing and Recording, Analyzing and Interpreting, and Communication and Teamwork). These rubrics are designed to be used independently of the Learning Context rubrics. You may choose to use one or more of these rubrics at various times throughout the year. It is not necessary to obtain evidence of student abilities related to these skills for every investigation.

You can use these rubrics as is, or modify them to meet your needs.

Balanced Assessment

Incorporating different types of assessment and evaluation strategies throughout a unit or topic provides each student with the opportunity to be assessed or evaluated as part of an ongoing process. Assessment in these cases is not an end in itself. In order to be responsive to student differences and to arrive at valid inferences about student achievement, it is imperative that you triangulate data using a variety of assessment strategies. Students must be provided with multiple opportunities to demonstrate the full extent of their learning, and these assessments should be fair, free from bias, and equitable for all (e.g., arranging accommodations, or using modified learning expectations for English language learners).

A balance of products, conversations, and observations should be considered when planning for assessment.

- Products include records of observations and results, graphic organizers, models, posters, illustrations, and audio or video recordings.
- Conversations include student conferences, interviews, dialogues, discussions, and oral questioning.
- Observations include scientific investigations, research skills, skill demonstrations, presentations, simulations, and drama activities.

Scientific and technological skills and processes provide one of the Foundations of Scientific Literacy. This foundation is discussed on pages 15 and 16 of *Science 2* (*Saskatchewan Curriculum,* 2011). This information provides you with a way of looking at what students can do so you can plan for further development of students' skills. In general terms, the skills involved are

- initiating and planning (e.g., formulating questions or hypotheses, and making predictions)

- performing and recording (e.g., conducting research, and safely conducting inquiries)
- analyzing and interpreting (e.g., evaluating and analyzing data, and drawing conclusions)
- communication and teamwork (e.g., using appropriate vocabulary, and communicating findings in a variety of ways)

Stages of Assessment

Assessment of *Learning (Summative Assessment)*

Assessment *of* learning is summative in purpose and occurs at the end of a period of learning. Summative assessment is evaluative; it is used to communicate and report to students, parents, guardians, and other stakeholders about students' progress in school.

Although assessment *of* learning occurs at the end of a period of learning, it is planned at the outset because it gives you information about student achievement of curriculum outcomes. Students need to be made aware in advance of which assessments are summative and what criteria will be used to assess their performance. Students should also have had practice with the assessment method(s) being used. Creating summative assessments that meet the needs of your students is easier with modifiable rubrics and unit tests. These are provided in the *Pearson Science* Program.

Summative evaluation applies a judgment to the data collected. These Assessment *of* Learning processes include *design projects* and *rubrics.* Summative evaluation informs you of how well the curriculum goals or outcomes/indicators for the unit have been met, and helps you determine the student's final reporting mark. The focus here has been on achievement of the outcomes by the end of the year. Consideration must be given to the achievement of outcomes that students master later in the year, but which were also assessed earlier in the year when achievement was less complete. Summative evaluation should reflect the latest level of achievement of the outcomes.

Assessment for *Learning*

In order to determine student readiness and prior knowledge, teachers usually begin the assessment cycle with assessment *for* learning. Units in the *Pearson Science* Program begin with an assessment *for* learning opportunity in the Unit Opener that is designed to activate prior knowledge, determine gaps in learning, uncover alternative understandings, and focus student learning.

Assessment *for* learning continues throughout the teaching and learning process. The teaching notes in this Teacher's Resource provide guidance if you are unsure of how to elicit student understandings of the various topics. The data from the assessment *for* learning may reveal a need to provide some foundational learning prior to moving individual students forward.

Assessment for *and* as *Learning (Formative Assessment)*

Formative assessment includes ways for you to gather, record, and interpret data about the progress and achievement of each student in the class. Moreover, assessment techniques that are fair and meaningful in the eyes of all shareholders—students, teachers, and parents—create a climate that will enhance students' motivation. *Observation records, journals and logs, drawings, audio and video recordings, student self-evaluation, interviews about projects,* and *student demonstrations and representations* all comprise formative assessment. Assessment should reflect the scientific and technological skills addressed in a particular activity.

The feedback to students occurs during the course of instruction and provides important and immediate information to them as they work. For you, systematic feedback provides invaluable insight into the need for program modifications. Thus, both assessment *for* learning and assessment *as* learning (*Science 2* (*Saskatchewan Curriculum,* 2011), p. 35) are formative in nature.

Research indicates that the most effective type of assessment for improving student learning is assessment *for* learning. What distinguishes one type of assessment tool from another depends on how it is used and what is done with the data it generates. For an assessment to be truly *for* learning, it must make a difference when you are planning for instruction and assessment of individuals or groups of students. If the assessment data you collect does not inform your instruction, then it is not assessment *for* learning.

Students also have a different role than in the past. Assessment *as* learning supports students learning about themselves as they self-assess, peer-assess, and set goals. Providing students with processing and reflecting time at the end of a class not only supports student understanding of the most recent concepts, but also helps students identify their own strengths and challenges as learners and recognize their growth over time. Developing metacognitive awareness enables students to take advantage of the choices provided within today's classroom.

Descriptive Feedback—An Important Assessment for Learning Tool

Feedback to students should be descriptive and specific whether it is written or verbal. "Good job" or "well done" is no more helpful than a check mark, a numerical mark, or telling a student "this needs improvement" or "you're not quite there yet." If something is well done, then you need to communicate exactly what was well done. For example, "The way you took care to draw exactly what you observed shows that you are recording like a scientist." Similarly, you need to communicate what specifically needs to be improved upon and offer suggestions to move struggling students forward. For example, "When demonstrating what you learned, you need to show *and* tell what you learned as if your audience doesn't know anything about liquids and solids."

Descriptive feedback is powerful assessment *for* learning. Research indicates that when teachers provide marks without comments or marks with comments, students do equally poorly. However, the same research indicates that providing comments only (with no marks) leads to significant increases in student achievement.

There are numerous opportunities for assessment *for* and *as* learning in this program that are supported by features in this Teacher's Resource.

In this Teacher's Resource

Teachers who are generalists may not be aware of what to look or listen for in student performances. In the Grades 1 and 2 Teacher's Resources, Assessment *for* Learning boxes list the evidence for you to look for in the form of questions and the learning targets for students in the form of simple statements.

While assessment, evaluation, and reporting will always serve the purpose of identifying levels of student performance, their major purpose is to support student growth and improve learning. This core belief must be alive in every classroom.

For further assistance with planning and assessment, refer to Hume, Karen. (2010). *Evidence to action: Engaging and teaching young adolescents through assessment* and *50 tools and techniques for classroom assessment*. Toronto: Pearson Canada. (a two-book package with over 100 modifiable line masters and 50 video clips).

References

Black, P., & Wiliam, D. (1998). Assessment and classroom learning. *Assessment in Education, 5*(1), 7–74.

Black, P., & Wiliam, D. (2001). *Inside the black box: Raising standards through classroom assessment*. London: King's College Department of Education & Professional Studies.

Stiggins, R.J., Arter, J.A., Chappuis, J. & Chappuis, S. (2004). *Classroom assessment for student learning: Doing it right–using it well*. Portland, OR: Assessment Training Institute.

3 Fostering Scientific Knowledge

Overview

Before you can give someone directions on how to get somewhere, you first have to know where they are.

The mind of the student is not like an empty storage bin, ready to be filled with new concepts and processes. Students in your classes come to you with different experiences and background knowledge in the three strands: life science, physical science, and Earth and space science. Before beginning instruction in any concept or skill, it is important to find out what your students already know and understand. This forms the basis of assessment *for* learning, and it also informs you of any preconceptions that students possess. You can, then, use this information as you plan for instruction.

Identifying Student Preconceptions

The Engage section of each lesson has two parts: (1) Activate and Build on Prior Knowledge and (2) Develop "I Wonder ..." Statements. This section reflects the Engage phase of inquiry. Asking effective questions during this part of the lesson can help you identify any preconceptions students have. In Jeff C. Marshall's article "Teaching Through Inquiry—Engage, Explore, Explain, and Extend," he suggests the use of the following questions: What do you know about ____? What have you seen like this? What have you heard about ____ that you aren't sure is true? As you record students' responses, mark any that students are unsure of with a question mark. After exploration and investigation of new concepts, have students reconsider the list of what they thought they knew before and correct any misconceptions. In this way, students have the opportunity to correct their own preconceptions based on the results of their investigations and direct experiences. This is much more powerful than simply telling them that what they thought they knew is incorrect.

The use of a K-W-L chart (What do I know? What do I want to know? What have I learned?) or a K-W-H-L chart (What do I know? What do I want to know? How do I find out? What have I learned?) is another way of identifying what background knowledge and preconceptions students bring to their learning. Templates for K-W-L and K-W-H-L charts are included as Generic Line Masters.

Pearson Science 1–2

Pearson Science 1–2 uses a straightforward, five-step method to help you deal with student preconceptions, as found in Driver and Oldham's book *Studies in Science Education.*

1. **Orientation:** The Unit Opener: Getting Started section in each unit starts students thinking about the topic.
2. **Elicitation:** The creation of the "I Wonder…" wall or bulletin board display during the Unit Opener encourages students to share what they wonder about the content of the unit. Developing "I Wonder …" statements in the Engage section of each lesson also facilitates elicitation. You can lead the class in additional activities, such as concept mapping or the use of a K-W-L or K-W-H-L chart, to further elicit student preconceptions. You can also have students make predictions before engaging in the activities of the unit.
3. **Restructuring:** The Engage sections orient students to the particular concept or topic in each lesson. Explore activities actively involve students in developing scientific and technological skills and processes in the four broad skill areas of initiating and planning, performing and recording, analyzing and interpreting, and communication and teamwork. This restructuring is more likely to take place when students predict the outcome of an experiment prior to the investigation and discuss the new things they have learned following the investigation. As you discuss with students the new things they have learned from the investigation, and encourage students to discuss these insights with each other, you help this restructuring to occur.
4. **Application:** Students apply their new views or conceptions to other areas or examples. The Explain section of each lesson provides these opportunities. The **open-ended project** in **Going Further** of the **Unit Closer** provides an opportunity for students to apply their ideas to a new problem.
5. **Review of Ideas:** Students solidify their new concepts by reviewing their new ideas in the Explain sections of each lesson.

References

Driver, R., & Oldham, V. (Eds.). (1986). *Studies in science education 13*, 105–122.

Marshall, J. (2013, July 18). Teaching through inquiry—Engage, explore, explain, and extend. *ASCD Express, 8*(21).

Developing Students' Skills

The Pan-Canadian Science Project, and the provincial curricula that have followed from it, emphasize students' understanding of basic concepts and development of skills. These skills include those necessary for conducting experiments and for designing and planning experiments, which are referred to as "skills of inquiry and design." Four broad skill areas are outlined in the Saskatchewan Science curriculum documents: Initiating and Planning, Performing and Recording, Analyzing and Interpreting, and Communicating and Teamwork. The *Pearson Science* Program is designed to facilitate acquisition in these skill areas.

To understand basic concepts and develop skills for doing experiments, students benefit from engagement in many hands-on activities that are well planned and organized. The *Pearson Science* Program provides a rich assortment of these activities that address the specific outcomes and indicators of the Saskatchewan Science curriculum documents. To develop skills of inquiry and design, students must design and plan investigations of their own. The Teacher's Resource suggests ways to provide opportunities for students to ask questions and devise investigations to answer their questions. Thus, students engage in the true processes of inquiry and design.

Inquiry Learning

The Saskatchewan Science curriculum regards inquiry as more than a systematic empirical process. Curriculum documents describe inquiry as *"a philosophical approach to teaching and learning, grounded in constructivist research and methods, which engages students in investigations that lead to disciplinary and interdisciplinary understanding"* (*Science 2* (*Saskatchewan Curriculum,* 2011), p. 7). The process builds on students' natural curiosity, providing them with opportunities for investigation, understanding, and reflection. The curriculum further states that *"Inquiry learning is not a step-by-step process, but rather a cyclical process, with various phases of the process being revisited and rethought as a result of students' discoveries, insights, and construction of new knowledge"* (*Science 2* (*Saskatchewan Curriculum,* 2011), p. 7).

Students using *Pearson Science Grades 1 and 2* will develop skills in being able to

- identify questions that can be answered through inquiry
- design and conduct investigations
- use appropriate tools and techniques to gather data
- analyze and interpret data
- develop explanations, predictions, and models using evidence
- think critically and make connections between evidence and explanations

- recognize alternative explanations and predictions
- use mathematics, where appropriate (e.g., measuring using non-standard units)

The development of questions that are broad in scope with possibilities for exploration is central to inquiry learning. Any of the four learning contexts may serve as curriculum entry points for inquiry.

- The scientific inquiry [SI] context may be used when students want an explanation for phenomena in their natural world. When students learn about liquids and solids in *Pearson Science 2*, they may pose questions about what happens when solids are mixed with liquids or how liquids flow when they are placed on different surfaces. Developing testable questions is the start of the inquiry process.
- The technological problem solving [TPS] context may be used when students wish to build something to solve a practical human problem. Learning about methods of altering and combining materials in the Using Objects and Materials unit in *Pearson Science 1* may lead students to wonder how they can create a useful object by selecting, combining, joining, and/or altering materials.
- The STSE decision making [DM] context may be used when students inquire about an issue that has scientific, technological, societal, or environmental connections. Topics such as how human activities can help or harm wild and domesticated animals, how people can contribute to protecting and improving the quality of air and water in their environment, how people can use what they know about liquids and solids to maintain a clean and healthy environment, and how aids support people's differing abilities to sense their environment all have STSE links that students may wish to investigate further.
- The cultural perspective [CP] context is addressed through the integration of Traditional Knowledge as a way of knowing about the world. Learning about the importance and sacredness of animals; how Indigenous peoples organize their understanding of living things; how daily and seasonal changes are represented through oral traditions and artistic works; the importance of air and water as elements in Mother Earth; and how the medicine wheel can be used as an organizer to represent the life cycles and seasonal behaviours of animals may lead students to ask questions about different ways of understanding and representing what they observe in their natural surroundings.

The Inquiry Process of Science

Opportunities for the inquiry process are integrated into the *Pearson Science 1 and 2* Programs. A simplified version of the systematic empirical inquiry process that appears in the *Pearson Science 3–5* Programs is used. The diagram below illustrates this process.

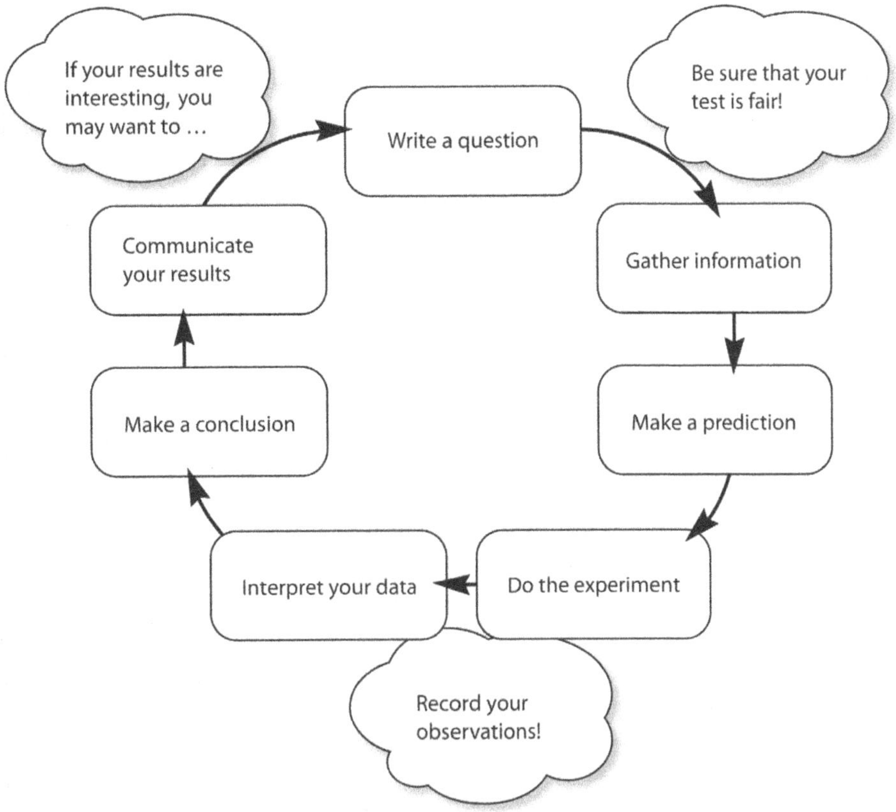

The inquiry process is also supported by the Scientific Skills Poster: Finding Out (refer to page 47 of this document). Note that these are only two representations of the inquiry process. It is important to be aware that there is not one correct scientific inquiry process. The steps can vary depending on what is being investigated; the circular pattern is typically used to keep an inquiry focused. For example, though predicting is typically placed after questioning, there is no reason that predicting cannot be completed after any step in an inquiry process. In some cases, it may not even be possible for a prediction to be made, for example, if results are inconclusive.

The Problem-solving Process for Technological Development

It is easy to confuse technology with science, since many of the applications of each are closely related. However, important differences exist between science and technology.

In Science ...	In Technology ...
we inquire about nature	we design solutions to problems of human needs
we conduct an experiment	we build something and test it out
we narrow down an investigation to find out the answer to one question	we broaden the design process to creatively come up with a variety of solutions
we should always get the same answer to the same question if we control the variables carefully	we may find many solutions and designs that solve the same problem

Pearson Science provides a problem-solving process for technological development based on several steps. A simplified version of the iterative problem-solving process that is illustrated in *Pearson Science 3–5* is shown below.

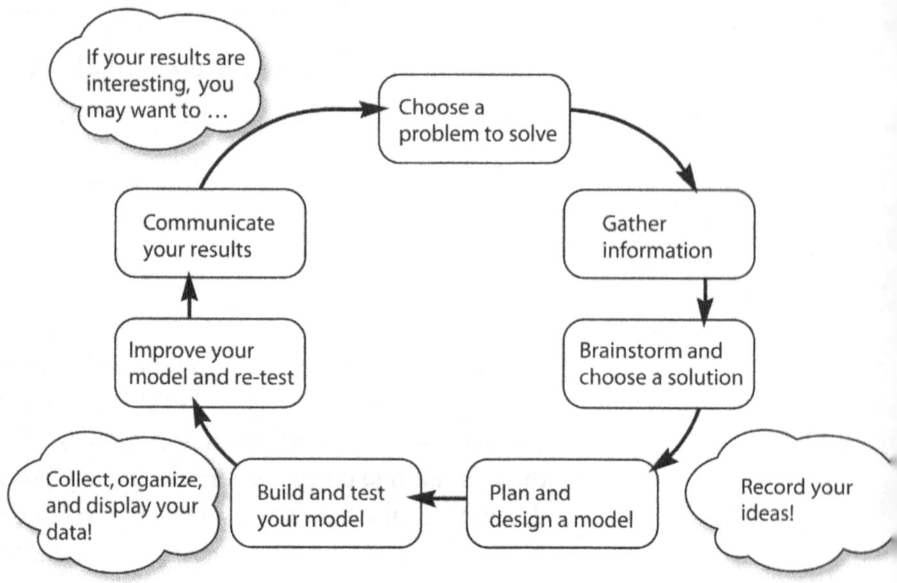

The Decision-making Process for STSE

Scientific knowledge can relate to understanding the connections among science, technology, society, and the environment. Students need to be able to see and understand the viewpoints of different stakeholders. A simplified version of the decision-making process that is illustrated in *Pearson Science 3–5* is provided below.

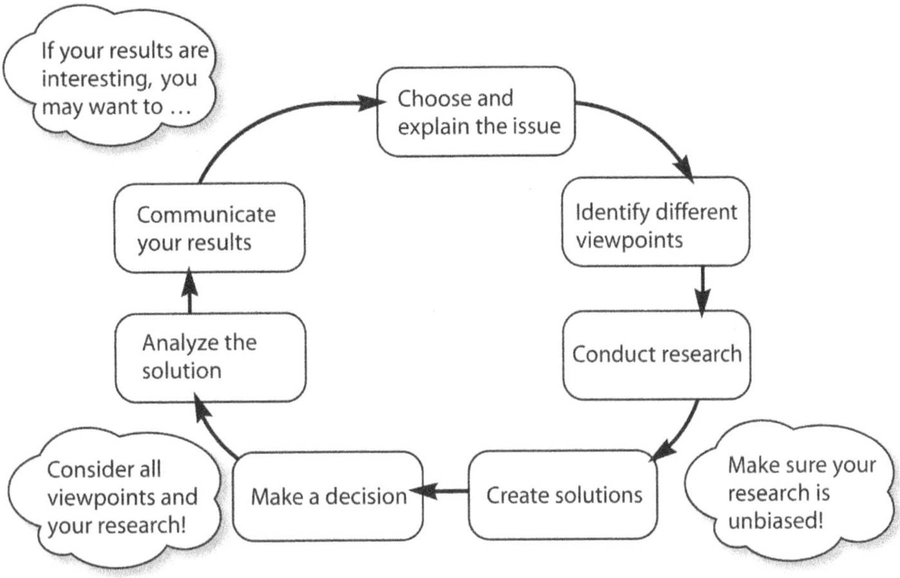

Purposeful Activities and Features

Each feature in the *Pearson Science* Program supports an aspect of the goals of science and technology and the development of scientifically and technologically literate students. Activities will occur through one or more of the four learning contexts: scientific inquiry [SI], technological problem solving [TPS], STSE decision making [DM], and cultural perspectives [CP].

- The **Unit Opener: Getting Started** introduces the unit through the formulation of "I Wonder …" statements that address the major concepts and skills encompassing the Big Ideas and Essential Questions of the curriculum. Students are also introduced to the fiction and non-fiction Little Books that will be used to develop the central ideas in each unit.
- **Core Learning Opportunities** include the **Engage**, **Explore**, and **Explain** sections, which correspond with the steps in the inquiry process. The activities in the **Engage** section activate and build on students' prior knowledge and personal connections and elicit "I Wonder …" queries about the content and focus of the lesson. The **Explore** section focuses on hands-on explorations and investigations.
    - Some Explore activities are **inquiry activities** that provide students with the opportunity to conduct and plan experiments. Through these activities, students will develop skills stressed through the learning context of scientific inquiry [SI].

(Grade 1: predicting the characteristics of common materials and testing predictions; investigating the sensitivity of different parts of the body to the touch of various materials; investigating changes in weather conditions that occur in daily and seasonal cycles.
Grade 2: investigating the properties of liquids and solids, changes of state, the relative viscosity of liquids, and the absorbency of different materials; investigating the effects of pushes and pulls on the motion of objects and the effects of different textured surfaces on the friction between two objects or surfaces; exploring air and water in the environment.)

- Some Explore activities are **design-and-build challenges** that provide opportunities to solve practical problems that arise from human needs or wants. Usually, students build a device to solve a problem through the learning context of technological problem solving [TPS].
(Grade 1: designing and constructing a useful object according to specific criteria by selecting, combining, joining, and/or altering materials; assessing the function of aids that support people's differing abilities to sense their environment.
Grade 2: building an object that will float, carry a load, and be stable; investigating technologies that are designed to make it easier for people and constructed objects to move on different surfaces.)
- Some Explore activities involve students in **exploration of the social, economic, environmental, ethical, and moral impacts of a real-world issue** related to the unit being studied. These activities occur through the learning context of STSE decision making. [DM]
(Grade 1: using materials appropriately and efficiently to the benefit of themselves, others, and the environment.
Grade 2: identifying ways in which humans can help or harm wild and domesticated animals; assessing ways in which people can use what they know about liquids and solids to maintain a clean and healthy environment.)
- Some Explore activities involve students in the **exploration of different ways of knowing and understanding the world**. These activities occur through the learning context of cultural perspective [CP].
(Grade 1: engaging in Indigenous ways of organizing understanding of living things; examining ways in which daily and seasonal changes are represented through oral traditions and artistic works.
Grade 2: recognizing the cyclic nature of Mother Earth expressed through the medicine wheel, including life cycles and seasonal changes of animals; examining the importance and sacredness of animals in First Nations, Métis, and other cultures; examining traditional objects that sink and float and that make it easier to move over different surfaces; recognizing the importance of air and water as elements of Mother Earth.)

- The **Explain** section provides further active learning experiences with a greater focus on sharing the results of student learning during the Explore activities. Activities in this section focus on demonstration of student learning and understanding.
- **Alternate Learning Opportunities** provide optional activities in the format of an **Activity Bank** for you to choose from to replace or supplement the Core Learning Opportunities and to meet students' needs, abilities, and/or interests. These activities provide additional opportunities to practise, apply, and/or extend the indicators for the lesson. They involve a variety of learning modalities, ability levels, and curricular connections.
- The **Unit Closer: Putting It All Together** takes students back to the learning targets from the start of the unit and the "I Wonder ..." statements they made over the course of the unit so they can reflect on their learning, and even extend their learning by developing inquiry investigations for any "I Wonder ..." queries that have not been answered.
- The Unit Closer also provides a unit task in **Going Further** that correlates with the Extend phase of the inquiry process. This task challenges students to use what they have learned in the unit to meet the requirements of a task that involves inquiry, technological problem solving, or decision making.
- Safety is emphasized throughout all hands-on activities.

The Process Skills of Science

The *Pearson Science* Program provides students with opportunities to explore the world around them and investigate questions through hands-on activities. As students engage in these activities and investigations, they develop and acquire the following process skills that form the foundation of scientific inquiry.

Observe: use the senses to gather information

Measure: use non-standard units to describe length, width, capacity, mass, volume, speed, and temperature of objects

Compare: identify similarities and differences

Classify: sort objects, events, or conditions according to predetermined criteria

Communicate: exchange ideas, knowledge, and questions through speaking, writing, presenting, listening, viewing, and reading

Infer: make assumptions based on reasoning

Predict: make decisions about what may happen based on first-hand experience or observations

Hypothesize: use observations and inferences to formulate possible explanations

Experiment/Investigate: plan and carry out investigations to test predictions or hypotheses

Controlling Variables: manipulate conditions to determine the effect of those conditions on the result of an experiment

Interpret: use collected information to draw conclusions

Making Models: represent objects by constructing replicas of them from different materials

Question: pose a question and research its answer

Scientific Skills Posters

The *Pearson Science* Program also provides support for the development of process skills of science through the Scientific Skills Posters. The Scientific Skills Posters provided with the units for Grades 1 and 2 are based on the *Saskatchewan Science Curriculum's* Foundations of Scientific Literacy. Specifically, the posters will help you introduce and expand on the following foundations:

- Foundation 3: Scientific and Technological Skills and Processes
- Foundation 4: Attitudes

Six of the eight posters provided for Grades 1 and 2 focus on skill areas that make up Foundation 3: Initiating and Planning, Performing and Recording, Analyzing and Interpreting, and Communication and Teamwork. The other two posters focus on the attitudes or stances of inquiry and safety found in Foundation 4, both of which are integral to success not only in science classrooms, but in all subject areas and later in the workplace.

Grade 1 Posters

Safety in Science Class (Attitudes)

This poster is an excellent tool to use as part of the year opener or Unit Opener discussion for any primary classroom. It is important for students to understand that observing and exploring with all their senses is how humans make sense of their world, but that doing so safely is essential to prevent injury to oneself and others. This poster could be reviewed at the beginning of the Using Our Senses unit. Before students plan or take part in any investigations in the classroom or on their own, they must understand that tasting and smelling unidentified substances should never happen without adult permission and that their eyes, ears, and bodies are precious and need to be protected during investigations. This poster will help reinforce these important points.

Finding Out (Inquiry) (Attitudes)

This poster addresses one of the Foundational Attitudes of Science. Similar to the safety poster, the overlying attitude that we want all students to develop is one of inquiry. Inquiry as an attitude in science means that students will come to a belief that scientific knowledge must have, at its base, the search for evidence to support a reasoned argument. In practice, this means that when students are investigating a question, they need to understand that predicting or even knowing a certain outcome is not enough. The evidence, reasons why, and how they know the outcome is true are just as important as the outcome itself. It is important to be aware that there is not one correct scientific inquiry process; steps may vary or be revisited depending on what is being investigated. The circular pattern is typically used to represent the inquiry process because of its recursive nature, but the process does not always occur in the same sequence of steps. For example, determining a question may come after learning new information, and predicting may occur at any stage of the process. You may choose to use this poster at the outset of any investigation done by students.

Observing and Recording (Scientific and Technological Skills and Processes)

This poster is designed to aid student understanding about making detailed observations, and then being able to compare and classify the information gained from their observations. You could use this poster before the portion of a unit in which students must investigate or explore a topic or question. Pre-teaching the vocabulary of detailed descriptors will help students be better able to clearly describe what they observe. The second part of the poster gives examples of how to record and organize observations. Drawing, labelling, charts, diagrams, photos, and even video can all be helpful tools for students to use. Introducing the options for classifying provided on the poster after the observations have been completed will allow students to assess the best ways to sort the information they have gathered. (Note that students should be taught to "waft" when they smell things in a lab setting. The student on this poster is smelling a pizza, so wafting is not necessary.)

Communicating and Teamwork (Scientific and Technological Skills and Processes)

You could use this poster as part of a Unit Opener discussion to review the skills involved in effective group work. It can also be used as a prelude to any group investigation to reinforce the expectations of group members.

Grade 2 Posters

A Fair Test (Scientific and Technological Skills and Processes)

This poster deals with collecting data and planning an investigation. This poster would be best introduced after an initial round of experimenting or testing. During an investigation, students often need to make modifications to their original plan or prototype. Before students make any changes to their experimental designs, they need to understand that changing more than one variable at a time will not help them understand which variable was responsible for the original problem or for a change in their results. Students should understand what is meant by a fair test. For a **fair test,** all the variables but one must be kept the same throughout the test; they are the **controlled variables**. The variable that is changed under experimental conditions is called the **manipulated** or **independent variable**. When only one variable is changed, a change in results can be connected to the changed variable. The variable that shows a change because of the experiment is called the **responding** or **dependent variable**. Students are also encouraged to repeat their experiments to verify their results.

Drawing Conclusions and Sharing Results (Scientific and Technological Skills and Processes)

This poster is intended to help students gain the foundational skills of analyzing and interpreting. This poster could be shared with students when they are looking at the results of an investigation or experiment, since it highlights the steps needed to decide whether their predictions were well-founded, whether they are ready to share their findings, and the best ways to share their results. Alternatively, during a unit like Motion and Relative Position, you could use this poster during the introduction to a final project to review the sequence of predicting, collecting data, reviewing results, and planning the best method of sharing of results.

Good science starts with good questions (Scientific and Technological Skills and Processes)

This poster is designed to help introduce the foundational skills of initiating and planning in science. Questioning and predicting may appear natural or simple for adults, but students often do not have the underlying skills or ability to explain their thinking well enough to produce good questions or predictions easily. Students often have many questions or very broad questions. Sometimes they have no question at all—they may just have an idea of a fun experiment they want to try. Likewise, their predictions may not always be linked to their past knowledge or to the question itself. At times they are not even predictions, but rather an answer they already know. Explain to students that their predictions should be based on a pattern that has been observed, and that predictions should be testable through investigation. You can use the "If … then … because …" format to help students with the thought process needed to create testable predictions that are connected to their past knowledge.

Reviewing this poster before the beginning of each science investigation or project will help develop good questions that will lead to more successful investigation experiences.

Classifying (Scientific and Technological Skills and Processes)

This poster is designed to support students' understanding of how to compare and sort the information they have gained from their observations. Students need to have the basic skill of classifying or sorting according to set criteria in science and in mathematics. Looking for similarities, differences, or a pattern in their observations is an important skill for students to develop and practise to experience success in more than one discipline. The second part of the poster gives examples of how to organize the items they have classified. Graphic organizers can help students with the sorting of their observations and help them see patterns in the items they have sorted.

4 Helping Students Relate Science and Technology to the World Outside the School

Overview

There are many ways to help students see real-life applications of science in the world outside the classroom. One of these is through field trips, be they to a natural environment such as a pond or park, or to a facility such as a factory, museum, or science centre. Most school divisions have instituted rules concerning field trips, which should be followed. Additionally, it is crucial that students fully understand the purpose of the trip in advance, and that they have specific information to obtain or questions to research.

Another way to relate science to the world outside is to have guests who are involved in some aspect of science as part of their career or hobby speak to the class. You may invite First Nations or Métis Elders and Traditional Knowledge Keepers into the classroom to share their wisdom on particular topics. Follow the appropriate protocol in contacting Elders and Traditional Knowledge Keepers (see below). Again, any division policies or guidelines about classroom visitors should be followed, and students should be responsible for preparing appropriate questions in advance and for thanking the visitor at the end.

Protocol for Contacting Elders and Traditional Knowledge Keepers

For most First Nations and Métis groups, transmission of knowledge (teaching) involves respect for that knowledge and its keeper. Often the teaching is given to anyone who asks and respects the protocol of the person being asked, but some knowledge is restricted and conditionally given only to a chosen few. Based on these practices, students (and teachers) need to understand a few basic rules of protocol (etiquette) in asking an Elder or Knowledge Keeper for help. The following is protocol to observe when asking an Elder or Knowledge Keeper for cultural or Traditional Knowledge.

1. **Ask about protocol.** Often it is wise to ask Elders about the protocols they use. They know that because you are not from their communities, you may not be familiar with their customs. They are more than happy to explain those protocols.
2. **Bring an appropriate gift or offering.** When one approaches an Elder, a Knowledge Keeper, or anyone who follows the traditional path, one needs to bring an appropriate gift or offering. For many First Nations and Métis people, tobacco is appropriate. Tobacco has been used for many generations as a type of offering. Many, if not all, First Nations and Métis people feel that tobacco is offered as a sign of respect. The amount of tobacco need not be significant; it can be as

little as a single cigarette. Jams and tea are offered in some communities (e.g., Air Ronge). The act of giving a gift or offering comes from the value of reciprocity—the belief in the act of giving and taking. Many First Nations and Métis groups practise this value since they believe that a teaching that is earned is valued much more than one that is given gratuitously. Often in ceremony, when an Elder or any practitioner asks Creator for help, he or she gives tobacco. Traditional drummers will offer tobacco to the Spirit in the animal who gave its life to make their drums.

The Elder or Knowledge Keeper will often consider your request before answering. Give the Elder time to reflect. If the Elder is able to help, he or she will keep your tobacco. If he or she returns the tobacco, the Elder cannot fulfill your request. Follow up the presentation of the offering with a handshake.

3. **Listen carefully.** If the request is granted, the answer one gets may teach through a story. Many Elders or Knowledge Keepers use the ethic of non-interference in their teaching. They do not give the teaching directly because they want learners to reflect and to discern the knowledge for themselves.
4. **Pay for their costs.** If you invite an Elder or Knowledge Keeper to your classroom, remember to offer gas money and an honorarium for their time, or if possible, arrange for transportation. Many Elders are aged, and many do not drive a vehicle.
5. **Be hospitable.** Offer tea (customary for many First Nations and Métis groups) and something to eat.

Other Tips

- One might call to arrange a visit with an Elder or Knowledge Keeper, but offer the tobacco in person and receive the teaching face to face. Never ask for the teaching directly on the phone. It is too impersonal.
- Learning from an Elder or Knowledge Keeper requires relationship building. Be accepting if the Elder refuses or can't fulfill your request. Some teachings are only given if the Elder feels that you are allowed to have that knowledge. For example, men may not ask women Elders for teachings on women and reproduction.
- Listen to what Elders or Knowledge Keepers do not say as much as to what they do say. If they seem to avoid a specific topic, there is a reason. They will not likely tell you the reason. It is for the listener to figure out or just accept.
- You may wish to contact your division office. Some divisions have Aboriginal coordinators or consultants who may already have resources at their disposal and be in contact with Elders or Knowledge Keepers. The office of the Treaty Commissioner retains a list of Elders who may wish to come and present to your classroom.

Cultural Perspectives

When teaching science, it is important to recognize that the cultural and religious backgrounds of students can often affect their perceptions. The students in today's Canadian classrooms are like threads woven together to create a multicultural social fabric. Each thread is unique and special. You should recognize that when science curriculum intersects with personal or family values, ethnic or cultural heritage, or religious traditions and beliefs, each student will have a unique response.

Rather than keeping science and personal values separate in the classroom, you can encourage students to explore their beliefs that pertain to science. You should encourage students to integrate their traditions or beliefs with points covered in the curriculum. In researching beliefs that pertain to their own traditions or those in a tradition with which they are less familiar, students have the opportunity to gain a deeper appreciation of how science is an evolving discipline that exists in conversation with, and not in isolation from, other areas of human existence. It is crucial for students to realize that their personal beliefs are respected, though these beliefs may differ from Western science perspectives. Students can interview parents, grandparents, First Nations or Métis Elders, priests, pastors, or other religious and cultural leaders and present their findings to the class. Students who do not have any particular belief system may wish to choose a religion or culture to research. Some important values that might emerge from this research include

- stories describing the cause of a particular aspect of the environment, such as the stars, rainbows, animal adaptations, or the creation of Earth
- belief in a higher supernatural force controlling the universe
- the concept that humans are stewards of Earth and responsible for it
- belief in the unity or oneness of all things

Values such as these are particularly important in helping students feel connected to and responsible for the environment, and in realizing that they can become scientists while preserving religious and cultural beliefs. This goal is especially important vis-à-vis First Nations and Métis students. By facilitating such discussion, you afford classmates of First Nations and Métis students the opportunity to learn about First Nations and Métis traditions and culture. By encouraging these discussions, research, and interviews, First Nations and Métis students may feel that their cultural identities are respected, and thus, pride in their heritage is supported.

"Theories of science are continually being tested, modified, and improved as new knowledge and theories supersede existing ones."
– Pan-Canadian Protocol for Collaboration on School Curriculum K–12, 1997

"[S]cience offers frameworks for explanations and control, which while also limited in scope, have been shown to possess particular explanatory power and which have thus become accepted by the scientific community and by society as a whole."
– Science Council of Canada, 1984

Encompassing Indigenous Perspectives in Teaching Science

The debate continues as to whether Eurocentric science can somehow coexist with Indigenous worldviews. The term *science education* in Western culture has no meaning in many Indigenous societies. Instead, other terms have been used to describe this realm: the "traditional ways of knowing," the "old knowledge," and the "cultural teachings." The recognition of differences between Indigenous perspectives and the Eurocentric viewpoint of science has influenced educators to examine the nature of Eurocentric science and its effects on Indigenous students' learning and attitudes, as Indigenous and scientific perspectives often seem to differ in terms of the social goals that are achieved. Historically, the Indigenous ways of knowing and sharing (scientific) knowledge are applied to ensure survival, whereas the Eurocentric perspective promotes gaining scientific/technological knowledge for the sake of knowing, and to exert power over nature and humans. The Indigenous view of coexisting with nature and celebrating its mysteries is juxtaposed with the Eurocentric scientific view and the need to explore and define everything in its path.

Indigenous individuals, as they are discussed in the *Pearson Science* Program, are denoted as First Nations and Métis peoples. This term encompasses a broader understanding of the unique traits, identities, cultural practices, and languages of Saskatchewan's various First Nations and Métis groups. In Saskatchewan, "First Nations and Métis" denotes various language groups and their respective dialects. The diverse language groups represented are the Denesųłiné (Dene), Métis, Nihithawak (Woodland Cree), Nēhinawak (Swampy Cree), Nēhiyawak (Plains Cree), Nakawēwiniwak (Saulteaux, Plains Ojibwa, or Anishinaabe), Očeti Šakowiŋ (sometimes referred to as Sioux, Assiniboine, or Stony; the Lakota, Dakota, and Nakota are part of this group.). Note that older titles in the *Pearson Science* series use the more common names, such as Woodland Cree. The names listed above are what Saskatchewan First Nations identify themselves as. An ongoing series of meetings with First Nations and Métis Elders has resulted in this more detailed description of the language groups. Be aware that the names listed in some of the older *Pearson Science* titles still reflect the more common names as opposed to the names that the various Nations identify themselves as.

Be aware that First Nations and Métis ways of knowing have many implications for the classroom. The *Pearson Science* Program enables teachers with varying ranges of knowledge about First Nations and Métis ways of knowing to achieve those outcomes and indicators. Moreover, th inclusion of First Nations and Métis content comes at a time when numbers of First Nations and Métis students are on the rise. With a greater percentage of First Nations and Métis students in the classroom, you are encouraged to empower these students through the exploration of their Traditional Knowledge, attitudes, values, and beliefs. Teachings on beliefs such as Spirit from First Nations and Métis perspectives, which are unquantifiable in scientific terms yet integral to their ways of knowing, cannot be divorced from the content but yet must be respected. Though these beliefs may be different from yours and those of Eurocentric science, the aim is to enrich *all* students and make them aware of other cultural perspectives. Though the Teacher's Resources specifically highlight First Nations and Métis teachings, exploration of various other cultural practices may be a benefit to all students. Lastly, significant attitudes toward the natural world can be imparted through rich dialogue and the perspectives highlighted in the Teacher's Resource. Though scientists and adherents of the Eurocentric science perspective may disagree with the spiritual beliefs in Traditional Knowledge and repudiate their "unscientific" way of understanding certain natural phenomena, it is difficult to object to the many values inherent in Indigenous Knowledge.

There are a few points to consider when you discuss the concept of Spirit.

- It is important to demonstrate respect for a view that may differ from our own. The way you model your respect for another paradigm even if it differs from your own is a crucial way in which you help students appreciate other viewpoints. A discussion on the differences in these views done in a respectful way may also help students appreciate how they might understand other views and question them without detracting from their legitimacy. To engender a positive discussion about an opposing point of view, refrain from framing a concept such as Spirit in a negative light, dismissing it as superstition, or viewing the belief as ignorance.
- If instead you express how such a perspective might benefit people of other beliefs and cultures, students might come to appreciate another's cultural worldview. Help your students appreciate how the view of all things as having a Spirit might be a benefit. How would one then treat an object, if one believes that object has a Spirit and is living? Would it engender greater respect? Would humans readily strip mine, clear-cut, exploit resources, and cause the destruction of habitat and extinction of species if they believed that all these resources were entities that had Spirit and life?

Values such as stewardship, responsibility, interconnectedness, and interdependence of humanity and the natural world abound in traditional stories and teachings but are also part of the science curriculum. Such values foster a love of learning and respect for nature. Our aims as educators are to foster scientific literacy and engender the development of responsible, caring, scientifically literate citizens. Encouraging students to understand the world from another people's perspective allows the development of tolerance and empathy and thus strives toward this conclusion.

The Indigenous worldview has long promoted keen observation and a knowledge and understanding of structures and designs, plants, celestial bodies, and ecological practices. Indigenous people still relay the Traditional Knowledge and teachings of their ancestors, and view this as a necessary means to ensure survival of their cultures and traditions. At the same time, it will be necessary to have competence in science to successfully participate in this highly technological society. As First Nations communities continue to grow, new scientific approaches and competencies may be realized by combining traditional ways with the new tools of science and technology to manage their environment and to promote economic growth into the next millennium. As educators, we can show not only things that are but also things that could be.

Special Considerations

Plural or Singular?

The decision to write "Indigenous peoples" or "Indigenous people" is important from an Indigenous perspective, as evidenced by a decade-long emotional battle in the United Nations over adding an "s" to a committee's name: the Committee on Indigenous Peoples. The use of the plural or singular depends on context, which is not always clear-cut. In a more formal context, the plural form recognizes the cultural heterogeneity among these diverse groups, and signifies an anti-stereotyping message. For example,

"Saskatchewan is home to First Nations and Métis peoples."
"During her visit to Canada, the Queen visited First Nations peoples."

This usage expresses the dignity of peoplehood of each single group. On the other hand, the singular form is appropriate when referring more informally to what people do or think, with an emphasis on individuals. For example,

"First Nations and Métis people want the best education for their children."
"Queen Elizabeth learned to ride a dogsled during a visit with First Nations people."

It is appropriate to write "Indigenous peoples worldwide have their own values" as well as "Indigenous people in my community have their own values." On a related topic, the term *First Nations* never has an apostrophe associated with it, even in the possessive case (e.g., "First Nations ways of thinking"), and it is always plural except when mentioning one specific nation, as in "Richard is from the Ojibwe First Nation." And lastly, "First Nations," "Aboriginal," and "Indigenous" are capitalized to dignify their recognition.

About Bison and Buffalo

A few of the *Pearson Science 1 and 2* Little Books show photos of bison (*Bison bison*). Some First Nations and Métis students may comment that these are buffalo.

When the first European colonists arrived in North America they likened the bison to buffalo, a bovine relative that they had seen in Africa and Asia. Traders, explorers, and colonists introduced the English term *buffalo* to First Nations through their interactions. Though each of the First Nations has its own word for this great animal in their respective languages, in English First Nations people have come to know and to call both plains and woodland bison as the plains and woodland buffalo. In contrast, scientists now classify the bison as a separate species in its own genus, as the taxonomical understanding of this animal changed. What used to be called *buffalo* in many science and history textbooks now are called *bison.* However, we respect and use the term *buffalo* in our resources since we respect the teachings that the Elders and Knowledge Keepers have given us. To many First Nations people the animal is sacred. They associate the name *buffalo* with this sacredness, and so they use the word when speaking English in prayers, ceremonies, and oral history. Among First Nations people words have power, and we respect their words. As a result, Elders will still refer to the buffalo when they pray. Special ceremonies as well retain the name *buffalo*. While we understand *bison* is the scientifically correct term, we also understand *buffalo* is the First Nations correct term to honour First Nations teachings.

Note: *Pearson Science 3–9* materials all have features and discussion of the medicine wheel. Our knowledge about the medicine wheel and other aspects of First Nations and Métis worldview develops over time and as additional titles in the series are completed. The change from the term *medicine wheel* to *Circle of Life* is the most up-to-date knowledge we have as of the printing of this title.

Medicine Wheel

A caution to the teacher:

The medicine wheel, originally an American Indian teaching, has been adopted by some First Nations people in Canada and has become part of their current teachings. The origin of medicine wheel teachings is unknown, and for some First Nations people, the expression *Circle of Life* is used instead.

Therefore, you are cautioned to be very careful not to generalize and to attribute the medicine wheel or medicine teachings to all First Nation cultures in Saskatchewan. These teachings may also vary from band to band, and from one family to another. Some First Nations people have medicine wheel teachings, the Nakawēwiniwak, for example, while others, such as the Oċeti Ṡaḱowiŋ, do not have any medicine wheel teachings at all. Instead, they have four-direction teachings.

Please also note that the colours of the medicine wheel vary in order and orientation, by quadrant and colour (blue instead of black) depending on the Nation. It is best to consult with your local First Nation, a resident Elder, a Knowledge Keeper, or your division expert or First Nations consultant before you teach about the medicine wheel in your area. It is wise to consult a knowledgeable source for your area as teachings are place-based. First Nations people are highly tolerant of, and curious about, the teachings and protocols of other First Nations groups. They generally don't take offence to an outsider inadvertently using the "wrong" expression; however, they do mind if an outsider ignores them when they point out what expression they use. First Nations people are extremely receptive and supportive of non-Indigenous people who want to learn from them.

Moreover, the medicine wheel teachings have been used synonymously with four-directions teachings in earlier materials, but again we caution teachers not to use them interchangeably. Our understanding of four-directions teachings has evolved as we work with Elders over time. Some Elders ascribe two additional directions to complete the four directions. These are upward toward the sky for Creator, down toward Earth for Mother Earth, in addition to the four cardinal directions.

For some Knowledge Keepers and Elders, the medicine wheel is more akin to a graphic organizer to help elucidate ideas than it is a teaching. Other Elders agree with the idea of the medicine wheel and its cyclic nature, but prefer the use of the word *circle*, as in Circle of Life. Circle of Life may be a good term to use if you don't know what the local teaching is on the medicine wheel, as the notion of Circle of Life has meaning in other cultures as well. In schools with populations of immigrant people this term may resonate with their culture, ideas, and beliefs. Hence, referring to the Circle of Life may be one way to engage students of all cultures into dialogue.

Pan-Indianism

Pan-Indianism is a term applied to the ascription of ideas, beliefs, worldviews, or ways of knowing to all First Nations people. The danger in the use of broad general terms is that we often stereotype First Nations even though we know practices, worldviews, ways of knowing, and beliefs vary from Nation to Nation, band to band, and sometimes from one family to the next. Thus, is it crucial that you describe where a teaching comes from and from whom it comes. *For example, Delvin Kanewiyakiho, a Cree Knowledge Keeper, taught me about lightning; his teachings passed on to him from his Elders are from Little Pine reserve....*

In cases where there are similarities among groups, note them as interesting but avoid sweeping terms such as "all First Nations people." *For example, some First Nations people lived as hunter/gatherer societies, though some did not.*

Another way to avoid stereotyping First Nations groups and their practices is to know what the local customs and practices are. Each family and each band used local resources to survive. This type of place-based teaching was passed on through oral tradition. When you take the time to learn what these placed-based teachings are, and can incorporate them into your teaching practices, it can help avoid spreading pan-Indian ideas.

Lastly, when you can, introduce examples of First Nations people in modern context to avoid the myth that all First Nations people, regardless of where they live, all dance and drum in Pow Wows, eat bannock, reside in lodges or tipis, paddle about in birchbark canoes, and hunt buffalo. For example, one person in contact with a number of Elders describes how some Elders he works with are more knowledgeable about cellphones and texting than he is. Many First Nations people believe that it is important to retain their language and their cultural customs, while at the same time contributing positively in every aspect of Canadian society.

Storytelling

Stories are a great way to relate a teaching. For many First Nations cultures, storytelling has been a vehicle to transmit ideas, teachings, values, and beliefs. When you use traditional stories in your lessons, caution must be taken. Avoid describing a traditional story as a legend or a myth. The words *myth* and *legend* denote an event that is unreal or fictional. For many First Nations groups, traditional stories are very real and are grounded in their beliefs and views about the world. In this way, these stories are very valid because they form part of their knowledge systems. These stories also have validity because they may describe a spiritual truth, understanding, or teaching, or pass on survival knowledge. Part of our responsibility as teachers is to help students understand these big ideas and to promote acceptance of other ways of knowing, even if they are different than our own.

There are certain protocols that surround teaching stories as well. For instance, among some First Nations groups, telling of traditional stories occurs only in winter. For other groups, only certain stories can be told when snow covers the ground. There are some stories that an Elder may give only to you and you may not share these stories, while other stories can be told to anyone. These protocols may apply to some First Nations groups but not others. Check with a local expert, consultant, or Elder about these protocols on storytelling for your area.

References

Allen, G., & Seumptewa, O. (1993). The need for strengthening Native American science and mathematics education. In S.J. Carey (Ed.), *Science for all cultures. A collection of articles from NSTA's journals* (pp. 38-43). Arlington, VA: National Science Teachers Association.

Ermine, W.J. (1995). Aboriginal epistemology. in M. Battiste and J. Barman (Eds.) *First Nations education in Canada: The circle unfolds.* Vancouver: UBC Press.

Peat, D. (1994). *Lighting the seventh fire*. New York: Carol Publishing Group.

Two Ways of Knowing Nature

by Glen Aikenhead

Two broadly different knowledge systems—scientific and Indigenous—can help us understand and deal with our physical world. They do not contradict each other; they can complement each other. They have similarities, differences, strengths, and limitations.

A fundamental similarity is that they are both anchored in the cultural milieu from which they originated and are currently sustained. Scientific ways of knowing nature arose and flourish within Euro-American cultures and largely portray a Eurocentric worldview. To function as a scientist, one must conduct oneself professionally in science's Eurocentric way. Similarly, Indigenous ways of knowing nature portray Indigenous worldviews. Moreover, both knowledge systems are systematically empirical, communal, continually revisable, rational, valid, and responsible for consequences generally valued by the cultural communities they serve.

Their differences arise from their respective worldviews. Science limits itself to the physical world, while Indigenous knowledge integrates the physical and metaphysical, which includes spirituality, among other things. Thus, the two knowledge systems are rational but in different common-sense ways. Although they are both empirically based, science emphasizes measurable data collected in relatively short periods of time, while Indigenous knowledge draws on both observable and intuitive metaphysical data. Because Indigenous "experiments" are based on natural changes in the local environment, they can take several generations to complete.

Science is communal and revisable because communities of scientists work toward producing agreed-upon representations of the physical world, sometimes called "scientific truth." These representations can change with new data or new ideas, if agreed upon by scientists through argument-based processes of consensus making (e.g., peer review) and if recorded in writing. On the other hand, Indigenous knowledge is orally and experientially passed down intergenerationally (e.g., through community activities, stories, dances, and other art forms) and is modified as experience dictates. Elders' ways of being in Mother Earth are a combination of accumulated wisdom and current local circumstances that need action to be taken for the community's survival in the physical and metaphysical world. This is sometimes called "wisdom in action." One contrast here is between intellectual representations that students can explore, describe, and memorize, and students learning to live wisely in nature. In short, science provides an intellectual view of the physical world while Indigenous knowledge concerns wise ways of being in Mother Earth (the physical and metaphysical world).

The way scientists see nature can appear to clash with the way Indigenous Elders inhabit nature. One way to acknowledge this difference is to appreciate the culture clashes that many Aboriginal students experience in school science, clashes between their own culture and the culture of science, which is embedded in science instruction. Worldview values and assumptions embraced by science can conflict with students' cultural views of the world.

Each knowledge system has particular strengths, but strengths can also be limitations. The holistic wisdom tradition of Indigenous knowledge is necessarily so complex that precise predictions rarely occur consistently in the short term. But in many fields of science, making accurate predictions is a strength. Experimental designs must be rigorous, results of experiments must be reproducible, and field studies must be replicated a sufficient number of times. This is accomplished by following a reductionist approach to inquiry in which scientists analytically reduce a complex phenomenon into simpler parts or variables amenable to measurement, conceptualization, and experimentation. Scientists assume that the "whole" can then be understood by putting together its parts. From an Indigenous worldview perspective, however, scientific reductionism is a severe limitation to knowing nature because it ignores a holistic understanding of the physical world, in which individual parts have meaning only in terms of their interrelationships with the whole of creation. Indigenous knowledge (wisdom in action) focuses on relationships among knowledge, people, and all of creation. Mother Earth is a web of interrelationships and the responsibilities that accompany each relationship.

Indigenous knowledge has proven its validity over tens of thousands of years through the survival of Indigenous people in extreme circumstances where harmony with nature pays off. Science has not been in existence long enough to test its validity with respect to human survival on Earth over a long span of time. But the validity of science with respect to its power over nature and its contribution to material progress is unquestionable.

Unlike the generalizable type of knowledge sought by science, Indigenous knowledge is place-based; its validity does not extend beyond the local environment inhabited by the people who hold that knowledge and whose cultural identity is intimately defined by that place. Place-based knowledge is intuitively sensitive to unique features of local phenomena (e.g., animal behaviour and river phenomena). Such unique features can be overlooked by scientists searching for quantifiable and generalizable patterns.

This is why some companies and government agencies employ Elders to join a team of scientists looking into issues of resource management, or the environmental impact of such developments as a new pipeline or mine. Scientists learn "Traditional Ecological Knowledge" (TEK) from the Elders on the team. This knowledge can be helpful to the company's or agency's decision on what to do. However, the Elders do not make the final decision. Sometimes they feel that their TEK is not understood adequately when their way of understanding the impact of a decision is at odds with the final decision taken.

Depending on their field of study, scientists conduct investigations using a variety of agreed-upon methods. The diversity within science is great. However, experimental scientists conform to such values as being honest and conscientious about the rigour of their experimental procedures, and being open to submitting their results for peer review, whenever possible. An acceptable result must be reproducible and must significantly add to scientists' knowledge of their field. There is also grea diversity among Indigenous peoples such that no one worldview can speak for all nations. Local variations are a part of a people's identity.

In summary, Indigenous knowledge is place-based, holistic, relational, spiritual, systematically empirical, continually revisable, rational, valid, and communal. It integrates the metaphysical and physical into one interrelated whole in which Spirit flows through relationships and responsibilities.

The Worldview of the Sweetgrass Cree First Nation

The worldview diagram of the Sweetgrass Cree people created by Traditional Knowledge Keeper Judy Bear has been included for your information on page 66. This diagram, as authorized by her Elders, depicts the worldview of her people, but it is general enough to extend to other First Nations groups. A detailed discussion is also included based on an interview with her on February 10, 2010. For Judy Bear, it is crucial that teachers appreciate the key aspects of a traditional worldview, and she believes that certain nuances may be lost on a reader without a detailed discussion. Therefore, key terms such as Traditional Knowledge, Traditional Knowledge Keeper, *and* worldview *have been defined.*

Defining Traditional Knowledge and Traditional Knowledge Keeper

First Nations peoples of Saskatchewan learned long ago how they fit into the natural world and its cycles. They adapted to the land instead of altering the land to accommodate them and their needs (Bear, 2010). That understanding has survived for millennia, passed down from generation to generation through oral tradition, and has become a keystone to a venerable way of life.

To understand that way of life, we must first define *Traditional Knowledge*. Judy Bear (2010) teaches that "traditional knowledge is imparted at a very early age. Traditional Knowledge involves the living of experiences such as ceremonies, the hearing of the stories, and the messages within them told to them by grandparents and other traditional people. Finally, Traditional Knowledge includes the act of passing down that knowledge, as it is recalled and transmitted through oral tradition." Thus, to be a Traditional Knowledge Keeper is to be a person who lives by the ideals of the culture, preserving the knowledge and passing it down to subsequent generations.

Understanding Traditional Worldview

A careful look at the integral components of Traditional Knowledge further elucidates our understanding of traditional worldview. Although many First Nations and Métis peoples have distinct cultural practices, languages, customs, protocols, and ceremonies, their cultures share many elements that help inform a generalized traditional worldview.

For many First Nations and Métis peoples, a worldview is more than simply a way of looking at the natural world; it is a belief system that encompasses relationships with Mother Earth, one's surroundings, and the things therein; but above all, worldview includes a relationship to Creator. Worldview includes the experiences, practices, and ceremonies of that particular people. The person is immersed in the beliefs and the values through ceremonies, language, and customs. Beliefs about the land and their relationship to Mother Earth and Creator become so natural that they permeate the actions, the ceremonies, the daily life, and the language of that people (Bear, 2010).

Another key component of worldview common to most First Nations and Métis people is the belief in the element of Spirit. Objects that scientists would class as non-living, such as rocks and fire, are in fact animate and are imbued with that very Spirit. Spirituality plays such an important role in the Cree culture, for example, that even their language, and its suffixes and prefixes, possess exact spiritual connotation (Bear, 2010).

The Worldview Diagram of the Sweetgrass Cree People Explained

The diagram entitled "The Worldview of the Sweetgrass Cree People" was a project done by Traditional Knowledge Keeper Judy Bear. It records beliefs and ideas given to her and authorized by her Elders.

Cree oral tradition provides an explanation for the sequence and order of living things in the worldview diagram. Although the Cree people believe that all things were created equally, life, as it unfolds, is not. This diagram helps teachers understand the general worldview of the Sweetgrass Cree people.

The diagram's most important piece, "Creator," is situated at the very top. For many Cree, to define Creator is unnecessary. For them, Creator is the creative force from which all things come is enough. For Judy Bear, "… it is enough to look around Mother Earth to see Creator in the grass and the butterflies" (Bear, 2010). On the tier immediately below Creator, we find Earth, Sun, Moon, and Stars. The Cree refer to Earth as "Mother Earth," for they liken Earth to a mother who nourishes and provides her children with everything they need for survival. The sacred elements of wind, water, fire, and rock extend from Earth. Under Earth in the diagram, we find plants. Plant life holds a very important place in the Cree belief system, since plant life provides everything that humans need to survive. Plant life affords food, shelter, and substances for healing. Moreover, some plants are considered sacred and are used in ceremonies. Four main plants are revered: tobacco, sage, sweetgrass, and cedar.

Tobacco, as it is commonly known and used for recreational smoking and often associated with lung cancer, is not the sacred plant mixture that was used in many Cree ceremonies. Hundreds of years ago, instead of tobacco, a plant mixture called *ciscēmās* [chis-shay-mas], made from dried bearberry leaves and other sacred plants, was used. This mixture was used in pipe ceremonies. Through trade, tobacco was obtained and used (Bear, 2010). The borrowed word *tobacco* was used as the English equivalent to denote the Cree word *ciscēmās*.

In the diagram, below plant life, small life forms, water and sky life, and land life (four- and two-legged) follow, respectively. Small life forms are living things that hop, burrow, and crawl (Bear, 2010), such as insects and earthworms. Water life includes all aquatic life forms such as fish, frogs, and turtles, while birds, such as eagles, hawks, and owls, make up the sky life. Land life includes both four-legged and two-legged beings.

Four-leggeds such as elk, buffalo, deer, and moose provide meat, shelter, and clothing. Last, we find the two-leggeds—humanity (Bear, 2010). There are many lessons that this diagram can teach us about our relationship with Earth. This worldview challenges the traditional Eurocentric view that Earth is to be used and its resources exploited. Many First Nations and Métis peoples may argue that stewardship is the only way to preserve the remaining natural world and though humans may need resources from the land, they must not destroy Earth in that pursuit. "Take only what is needed and give back" is the adage by which the First Nations have lived for countless millennia. The offering of tobacco is an expression of this belief and a practice of the value of reciprocity. This way of looking at the natural world imparts a wisdom passed down for many generations. It teaches its adherents to value Earth, to respect it, and to live harmoniously within it. In short, the diagram illustrates a way of life that is sustainable.

First Nations Historical Worldview

Tāpwēwakēyihtamōwin-pimātisiwin-cycle of life

"As long as the sun shines, the grass grows and the water flows"

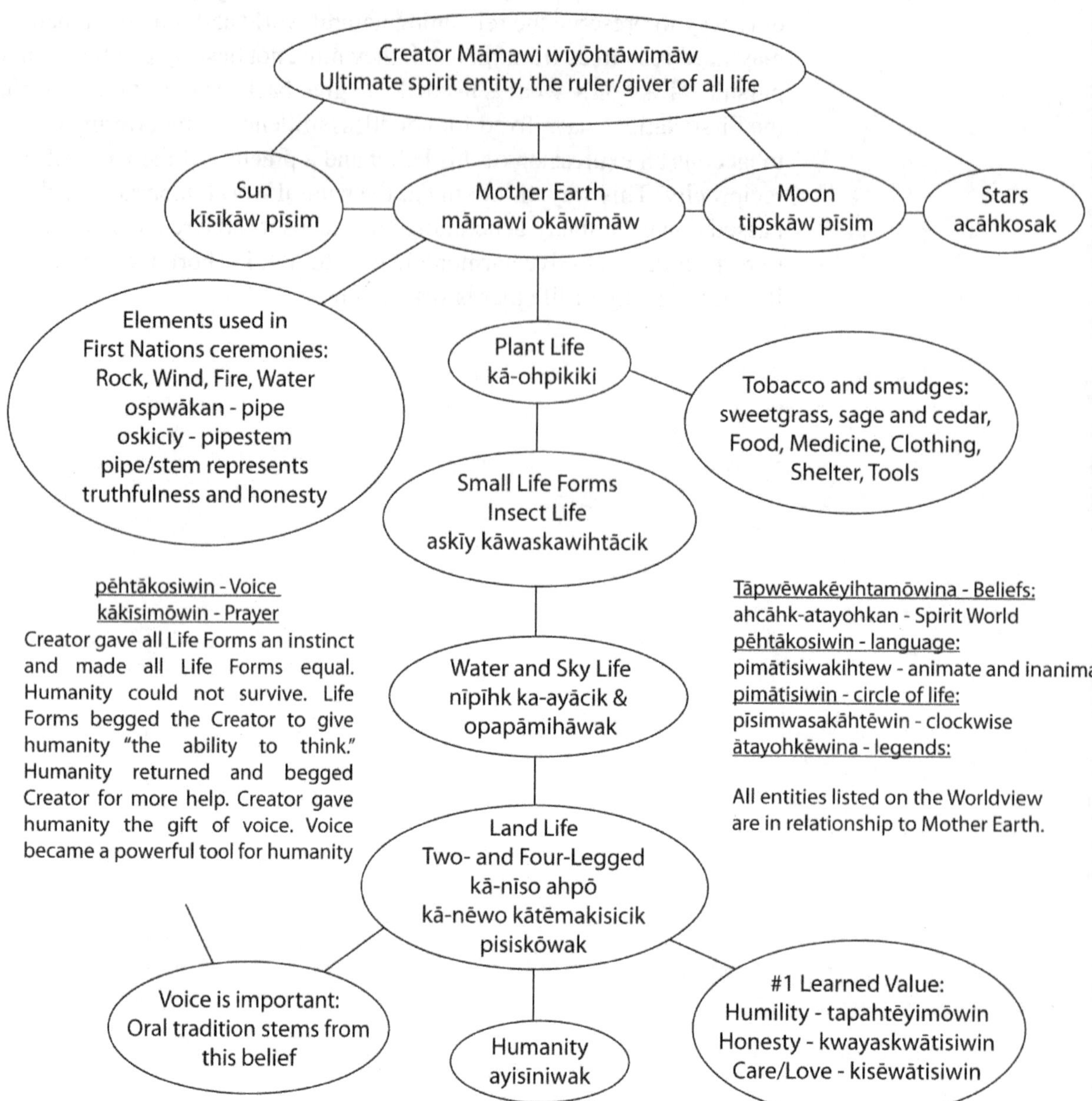

Traditional teaching — learning takes place before birth:
The mother shapes the unborn child's emotions, transfers feelings such as Love, Caring and Compassion.
Each part in this Worldview is a Teaching.

Written by Judy Bear, sanctioned by her consultant Elders
Based on the First Nations People oral traditions.
Used with permission.

5 Encouraging Responsible Attitudes in Science

Student Attitudes

One of the four foundations of the Pan-Canadian Common Framework of Science Learning Outcomes focuses on student attitudes toward science:

Students will be encouraged to develop attitudes that support the responsible acquisition and application of scientific and technological knowledge to the mutual benefit of self, society, and the environment.
– Common Framework of Science Learning Outcomes, p. 19

The Framework defines attitudes as "generalized aspects of behaviour that are modelled for students by example and reinforced by selective approval." In short, you are a role model for students. It is what you do more than what you say that influences students' attitudes toward science. Through your behaviour, students will become interested in science and form positive attitudes toward it.

Most students are eager to discover how and why things work and to learn about their environment. Educators must nurture and encourage this natural curiosity and love of inquiry to develop a positive attitude to science in children. According to the Framework, "science education can contribute to attitudinal growth when …

- students are encouraged to examine how science has an impact daily and over the long term on themselves and on the lives of others …
- students are involved in science investigations and activities that stimulate their interest and curiosity …
- students are provided with opportunities for development, reinforcement, and extension of attitudes that support scientific inquiry …
- students are provided opportunities to work in group situations on real-life problems …
- students are involved in activities that encourage responsible action toward living things and the environment and encouraged to consider issues related to sustainability from a variety of perspectives …
- students are encouraged to assess and manage potential dangers and apply safety procedures …"

The activities and sections in the *Pearson Science* Program provide several opportunities for students to develop positive attitudes toward science in all of these ways. Within the units, students

- look at how science topics affect their daily lives
- work on thought-provoking activities and investigations designed to stimulate their curiosity

- develop inquiry skills by formulating questions of their own and designing inquiries to investigate them
- collaborate with partners and groups on activities and investigations
- are encouraged to respect living things, as well as the environment
- learn about safety procedures and put them in practice

Safety

When it comes to safety in the science classroom, the safety of students and teachers is a primary concern of Pearson Canada. Safety requires that you model appropriate behaviour in the classroom, are aware of safety procedures and regulations, and provide students with safe learning environments. It is important to establish safety procedures with the class before you begin a science unit and to reinforce them on a regular basis. The Scientific Skills Poster—Safety in Science Class—provides visual and textual reminders of "safety-first" behaviours.

Throughout the *Pearson Science* Program, activities give safety instructions for the student and you where appropriate. The Grade 2 Teacher's Resource provides a lesson about WHMIS symbols in the Liquids and Solids unit.

The intention is for you to use the following information about safety issues in the school science classroom when you are preparing for a lab activity and planning demonstrations. Because this is an overview, it cannot be a comprehensive coverage of everything related to school science safety. Pearson Canada takes no responsibility for the completeness of this information or for the implementation of these suggestions.

Teachers are encouraged to practise the four Ps of safety. Use the guidelines of Kwan and Texley (2003):

Prepare

- Keep up to date with your personal safety knowledge and certifications.
- Be aware of national, provincial, division, and school-level safety policies and guidelines.
- Create a safety contract with students.

Plan

- Develop learning plans that ensure all students learn effectively and safely.
- Choose activities that are best suited to the learning styles, maturity, and behaviour of all students and that include all students.
- Create safety checklists for in-class activities and field studies.

Prevent

- Assess and mitigate hazards.
- Review procedures for accident prevention with students.
- Teach and review safety procedures with students, including the need for appropriate clothing.
- Do not use defective or unsafe equipment or procedures.
- Do not allow students to eat or drink in science areas.

Protect

- Ensure students have sufficient protective devices, such as safety glasses.
- Demonstrate and instruct students on the proper use of safety equipment and protective gear.
- Model safe practice by insisting that all students and visitors use appropriate protective devices.

The following safety suggestions are intended to help establish increased safety awareness for staff and students.

Safety Equipment

- Maintain and check all safety equipment regularly.
- Keep a first-aid kit stocked and available.
- Use hot plates in lieu of open flames as often as possible.

Safety Procedures for Teachers

Although reviewing safety guidelines may be a part of your initial class, safety should be an integral part of your classroom and procedures at all times. Science and Technology teachers should always

- model safe practices at all times (e.g., wear safety goggles when appropriate)
- be able to see the whole class if working with something potentially harmful (i.e., do not become engrossed in a discussion with one student)
- ensure all safety equipment (including first-aid kit) is available, in working order, and checked regularly
- arrange the classroom furnishings so that people are not tripping over knapsacks as they move about the room
- teach students the correct use of all tools and equipment before they use them
- use digital or non-mercury thermometers
- buy ample and appropriate safety equipment for the lab (e.g., have more than enough safety goggles in smaller sizes)
- dispose of any broken glass in a dedicated container kept out of the way and clearly labelled
- dispose of batteries, oils, etc., in appropriate ways
- show students how to safely smell substances (i.e., have them use their hands to waft the scent toward their noses)
- explain that students should not taste non-food substances
- label all chemicals used in experiments, even vinegar and baking soda
- use hot plates or microwaves instead of Bunsen burners whenever possible
- ventilate the classroom when using or producing gases or fumes (e.g., when using hot-glue guns)
- allow hot plates time to cool off before moving them

- demonstrate and teach students to handle all materials safely; use plastic containers instead of glass when applicable
- become certified in CPR and emergency first aid
- smooth sharp edges of glass mirrors with duct tape
- be aware of student allergies (foods, plants, animals, latex, environmental) and asthma
- be careful of plants in the room because some students may have allergies and some plants are poisonous
- choose pets for your classroom carefully, as some pets carry diseases or cause allergies (see the Living Things in the Classroom section on page 71 of this Program Overview)
- supervise students closely when they are using electricity or heat (small groups are easier to supervise than individuals or partners; depending on the students and the hazards involved, a teacher demonstration may be the best teaching strategy to use)
- circulate around the class to observe students, and correct procedures by demonstration if necessary
- have students do procedures that produce fumes, such as gluing or sanding, only in areas with adequate ventilation

Safety Procedures for Students

In addition to using their common sense, students may need to review these safety rules/procedures.

- Know the emergency fire exit route.
- Keep your work area uncluttered and organized.
- If you have long or loose hair, tie it back. Roll up long sleeves.
- Make your teacher aware of any safety concerns, including allergies or medical conditions.
- Follow instructions carefully.
- Always wear safety goggles as requested by your teacher.
- Do not leave any experiment unattended.
- Never smell any material or substance directly. Instead, gently wave your hand over it to bring its vapours toward your nose.
- Do not eat during science investigations.
- Do not taste liquids unless told to do so by your teacher.
- Do not engage in horseplay when conducting experiments.
- Direct flying devices away from yourself and other classmates.
- Never stare directly at bright light sources such as the Sun or laser pointers.
- Learn to recognize warning symbols.
- Heat solids and liquids only in heat-resistant glass beakers and test tubes.
- Heat glass containers only if they are Pyrex or Kimax.
- Never use broken or cracked glassware.
- Report broken glass or spills to your teacher immediately.
- When you have finished an experiment, clean all the equipment before putting it away.

- Be careful with hot plates and pieces of equipment that have been heated, since they may take a long time to cool down.
- Always wash your hands well with soap—preferably liquid—after handling chemicals, soil, plants, or animals.
- Make sure that any water or wet hands are kept away from electrical outlets.

Living Things in the Classroom

Using living things in the classroom can enhance a science program and may expose students to a new experience. Check your division's policy for the care of plants and animals and observe the following general considerations.

- Do not use live vertebrate animals for experimental purposes (i.e., for experimenting with living conditions or food requirements).
- Keep living things in containers or facilities that ensure their safety and students' safety.
- Do not keep wild vertebrates, turtles, or birds (or birds' nests) in the classroom, as they may transmit disease.
- Ensure that students always wash their hands thoroughly after handling plants, animals, soil, or chemicals.
- Have students wear disposable gloves when cleaning animal cages.
- Invertebrates such as mealworms, earthworms, and caterpillars are ideal for classroom use because they do not transmit disease and are easily acquired. Have students practise respect for living things and the environment by returning the invertebrates to their habitat when the investigation is complete.
- When purchasing classroom pets, ensure you are buying them from a reputable dealer who will supply disease-free stock.

Respect for the Environment

When you conduct a field trip and observe or collect materials outdoors, you are a role model for students. You can model respect for the environment in the following ways.

- Collect samples from places that are public property, or obtain permission to remove samples from private property.
- Put objects such as rocks and soil back where they were collected when the investigation is complete.
- If possible, draw pictures and take photographs of animals, insects, and plants rather than bringing them back to class.
- If the above is not possible, collect samples of plants, animals, and insects in ways that do not harm them.
- Return animals and insects to their habitats as soon as possible.
- Ensure the areas you visit are cleaner when you leave than when you arrived. Leave only your footsteps.
- Reduce, reuse, and recycle materials in your classroom.

Pearson Science 1–2
Teacher's Resource—Generic Line Masters

Assessment Rubrics

Learning Contexts

Inquiry Skills

Program Masters

Inquiry Skills

Recording and Sorting Information

Name: ______________________

Scientific Inquiry

	Level 1	Level 2	Level 3	Level 4
Knowledge				
Understanding of Concepts	Student demonstrates limited understanding of science concepts related to the topic.	Student demonstrates some understanding of science concepts related to the topic.	Student demonstrates considerable understanding of science concepts related to the topic.	Student demonstrates thorough understanding of science concepts related to the topic.
Skills				
Initiating and Planning • Posing questions • Designing inquiry	Student requires significant guidance and support to plan for inquiry.	Student poses a question and creates inquiry plans related to the problem with some guidance and support.	Student poses a testable question and makes a prediction related to inquiry topic; materials and procedure relate to the question.	Student inquiry plans include a testable question and prediction, materials, a sequential procedure, and possible relationships among variables.
Performing and Recording • Collecting data • Recording data	Student is able to use tools and equipment, follow the steps of the procedure, collect data, and record information in an organized manner (using tables, numbers, etc., as modelled) with significant guidance and support.	Student is able to use tools and equipment, follow the steps of the procedure, collect data, and record information in an organized manner (using tables, numbers, etc., as modelled) with some support.	Student is able to use tools and equipment as shown, follow the steps of the procedure, collect data, and record information in an organized manner (using tables, numbers, etc., as modelled) independently.	Student uses tools and equipment effectively and appropriately, contributes to the planning of the procedure and data collection, records data in an organized manner (using tables, numbers, etc., as modelled), and makes observations and notes about other evidence.
Analyzing and Interpreting • Identifying patterns in data • Proposing explanations	Student is able to organize data collected and identify patterns with significant guidance and support.	Student is able to organize data and identify patterns with some guidance and support.	Student is able to organize data, identify some patterns, and propose explanations independently.	Student is able to organize data, identify patterns, and propose explanations with considerable insight.
Communication and Teamwork • Stating conclusion • Sharing results	Student is able to reach a simple conclusion based on findings and communicate results with significant guidance and support.	Student is able to reach a conclusion based on findings and communicate results with some guidance and support.	Student is able to reach a conclusion based on findings and communicate results independently.	Student is able to reach a conclusion based on findings and communicate results effectively and with deep understanding.

	Level 1	Level 2	Level 3	Level 4
STSE				
Nature of Science and Technology	Student demonstrates little recognition that science knowledge results from systematic testing of ideas.	Student demonstrates some recognition that science knowledge results from systematic testing of ideas.	Student demonstrates considerable recognition that science knowledge results from systematic testing of ideas.	Student demonstrat a high degree of recognition that science knowledge results from systematic testing o ideas.
Social and Environmental Contexts of Science and Technology	Student shows little recognition that there are social and environmental connections to the inquiry.	Student shows some recognition that there are social and environmental connections to the inquiry.	Student can suggest social connections and environmental connections to the inquiry when guided to do so.	Student suggests social connections and environmental considerations to th inquiry independently.
Attitudes				
Interest in Science • Obtaining hands-on experience • Observing during class and on field trips • Reading, watching, and listening	Student demonstrates little curiosity in the content area, in familiar contexts.	Student demonstrates some curiosity in the content area, in familiar contexts.	Student clearly demonstrates curiosity in the content area, in familiar and unfamiliar contexts.	Student demonstrat a high degree of curiosity in the content area, in familiar and unfamiliar contexts.
Inquiry in Science	Student shows little understanding of the need for evidence.	Student shows some understanding of the need for evidence related to the question or purpose.	Student recognizes the need for evidence that either supports or refutes the prediction or purpose.	Student recognizes the need for accurac and precision in collecting relevant evidence to support or refute the prediction or purpose.
Collaboration • Co-operating with classmates	Student works in a group throughout the inquiry process with significant guidance.	Student works in a group and contributes to the group during the inquiry process with some guidance.	Student contributes and listens to the group throughout the inquiry process independently.	Student contributes to the group and considers and builds on the contribution of other members throughout the inquiry process.
Safety • Considering self and other students • Considering plants and animals	Student demonstrates limited concern for safety with respect to self, other students, and/or live specimens.	Student demonstrates some concern for safety with respect to self, other students, and/or live specimens, including the use of protective devices as appropriate.	Student demonstrates concern for safety with respect to self, other students, and/or live specimens, including the use of protective devices as appropriate.	Student demonstrate high degree of recognition of the need for safety with respect to self, other students, and/or live specimens, includin the use of protective devices as appropriate.

Name: ______________________

Technological Problem Solving

	Level 1	Level 2	Level 3	Level 4
Knowledge				
Understanding of Concepts	Student demonstrates limited understanding of the scientific principles and technological processes related to the problem.	Student demonstrates some understanding of the scientific principles and technological processes related to the problem.	Student demonstrates considerable understanding of the scientific principles and technological processes related to the problem.	Student demonstrates thorough understanding of the scientific principles and technological processes related to the problem.
Skills				
Initiating and Planning • Identifying a practical problem • Developing possible solutions	Student identifies a practical problem and comes up with a solution and procedure with significant guidance and support.	Student identifies a practical problem and comes up with a solution and procedure with some guidance and support.	Student identifies a practical problem, generates a solution, and develops a simple procedure independently.	Student identifies a practical problem, generates several solutions, selects a solution from several alternatives, and develops a detailed procedure.
Performing and Recording • Building a prototype • Carrying out a plan of action	Student builds a prototype or carries out a plan of action with significant assistance.	Student builds a prototype or carries out a plan of action with some assistance or limited effectiveness.	Student builds a prototype or carries out a plan of action independently with considerable effectiveness.	Student builds a prototype or carries out a plan of action independently with a high degree of effectiveness.
Analyzing and Interpreting • Testing the prototype/plan of action (if applicable)	Student tests and evaluates whether the prototype/plan of action works with significant guidance and support.	Student tests and evaluates whether the prototype/plan of action works with some guidance and support.	Student tests and evaluates whether the prototype/plan of action works independently.	Student makes modifications as a result of testing and then retests the improved prototype/plan of action.
Communication and Teamwork • Designing and developing the solution	Student contributes to the team with significant guidance and support.	Student contributes to the team in the development, testing, and evaluation of a technological solution with some guidance and support.	Student contributes to the team in the development, testing, and evaluation of a technological solution independently.	Student contributes to the team and takes on a leadership role in the development, testing, and evaluation of a technological solution.

	Level 1	Level 2	Level 3	Level 4
STSE				
Nature of Science and Technology	Student does not distinguish between science and technology, even with assistance.	Student distinguishes between scientific ideas and technological solutions with assistance.	Student distinguishes between scientific ideas and technological solutions independently.	Student understands processes used in science and technology to develc technological solutions.
Relationship Between Science and Technology	Student expresses ideas for using technology to meet a human need with significant guidance and support.	Student expresses ideas for using technology to meet a human need with some guidance and support.	Student expresses ideas for using technology to meet a human need independently.	Student shows sounc understanding of the connection between science and technological problems.
Social and Environmental Contexts	Student demonstrates limited understanding of the social and environmental implications of the technology.	Student demonstrates some understanding of the social and environmental implications of the technology.	Student demonstrates considerable understanding of the social and environmental implications of the technology.	Student demonstrate a high degree of understanding of the social and environmental implications of the technology.
Attitudes				
Collaboration • Co-operating with other students	Student works with other students to solve problem with significant guidance and assistance.	Student works with other students to solve problem and collaborates with other students with some guidance and assistance.	Student collaborates with other students for portions of the problem-solving process.	Student collaborates effectively with oth students throughout all aspects of the problem-solving process.
Stewardship • Demonstrating the need for stewardship	Prototype development or plan of action shows limited understanding of the need for environmental stewardship.	Prototype development or plan of action shows some understanding of the need for environmental stewardship.	Prototype development or plan of action shows considerable understanding of the need for environmental stewardship.	Prototype development or plar of action shows significant understanding of the need for environmental stewardship.
Safety • Concerning self and others	Student demonstrates limited concern for the safety of self and others.	Student demonstrates some concern for the safety of self and others.	Student demonstrates considerable concern for the safety of self and others.	Student demonstrate a high degree of concern for the safet of self and others.

Name: ______________________

STSE Decision Making

	Level 1	Level 2	Level 3	Level 4
Knowledge				
Understanding of Concepts	Student shows limited understanding of the science, technology, societal, and environmental concepts related to the issue.	Student shows some understanding of the science, technology, societal, and environmental concepts related to the issue.	Student shows considerable understanding of the science, technology, societal, and environmental concepts related to the issue.	Student shows thorough understanding of the science, technology, societal, and environmental concepts related to the issue.
Skills				
Initiating and Planning • Identifying an issue • Planning research	Student struggles to recognize an issue and propose a solution, even with significant guidance and support.	Student identifies an issue and proposes a solution with some guidance and support.	Student identifies an issue and proposes a solution independently.	Student clarifies an issue and develops a plan to address the issue.
Performing and Recording • Identifying stakeholders • Acquiring and evaluating information	Student recognizes different points of view with significant guidance and support.	Student recognizes different points of view with some guidance and support.	Student recognizes different points of view and is able to suggest ways of finding information about the points of view of different stakeholders.	Student recognizes points of view of different stakeholders and is able to research and document information about an issue from different sources.
Analyzing and Interpreting • Generating courses of action • Creating a plan • Assessing impact of action	Student chooses a course of action from a list of possibilities with guidance and support.	Student chooses a course of action from a list of possibilities.	Student evaluates the pros and cons of possible actions and chooses an action from a list of possibilities.	Student evaluates the pros and cons of possible actions, and chooses a course of action based on criteria.
Communication and Teamwork • Implementing decision or plan of action • Reporting (oral or written)	Student reports on the decision or plan of action of the team with significant guidance and support.	Student communicates within the team and reports on the decision or plan of action of the team with some guidance and support.	Student communicates within the team and reports on the decision or plan of action of the team independently.	Student communicates effectively within the team and reports on the decision or plan of action of the team, reflecting on the process.

	Level 1	Level 2	Level 3	Level 4
STSE				
Nature of Science and Technology	Student shows little recognition that there are connections between societal issues and the development of technologies and scientific knowledge.	Student shows some recognition that there are connections between societal issues and the development of technologies and scientific knowledge.	Student recognizes and makes connections between societal issues and the development of technologies and scientific knowledge.	Student understands and makes connections betwee societal issues and the development of technologies and scientific knowledg
Social and Environmental Contexts of Science and Technology	Student demonstrates little understanding that society and the environment must be considered in decision making related to issues.	Student demonstrates some understanding that society and the environment must be considered in decision making related to issues.	Student demonstrates clear understanding that society and the environment must be considered in decision making related to issues.	Student demonstrat deep understanding that society and the environment must b considered in decision making related to issues.
Attitudes				
Collaboration • Researching • Choosing alternatives • Implementing plan	Student works in a group with significant guidance and assistance.	Student contributes to group with some guidance and assistance.	Student contributes and listens to group.	Student contributes to group and considers and builds on the contributions of other members.
Stewardship • Researching • Planning • Assessing • Reporting	Student demonstrates limited understanding of the implications of decisions in relation to society or the natural environment.	Student demonstrates some understanding of the implications of decisions in relation to society and the natural environment.	Student demonstrates clear understanding of the implications of decisions in relation to society and the natural environment.	Student demonstrate deep understanding of the implications c decisions in relation to society and the natural environment
Appreciation of Science • Understanding our world • Differing perspectives	Student recognizes that there could be more than one perspective related to an issue with significant guidance and support.	Student recognizes that different perspectives must be taken into consideration in the decision-making process with some guidance and support.	Student recognizes different perspectives in the decision-making process independently.	Student takes into consideration different perspective in the decision-making process.

Name: ____________________

Cultural Perspectives

	Level 1	Level 2	Level 3	Level 4
Knowledge				
Understanding Key Science Concepts	Student demonstrates limited understanding of science concepts related to the topic.	Student demonstrates some understanding of science concepts related to the topic.	Student demonstrates sound understanding of science concepts related to the topic.	Student demonstrates excellent understanding of science concepts related to the topic.
Understanding Key Cultural Knowledge	Student demonstrates limited understanding of Indigenous or other cultural knowledge related to the topic.	Student demonstrates some understanding of Indigenous or other cultural knowledge related to the topic.	Student demonstrates sound understanding of Indigenous or other cultural knowledge related to the topic.	Student demonstrates excellent understanding of Indigenous or other cultural knowledge related to the topic.
Skills				
Initiating and Planning • Posing questions • Planning investigations	Student approaches inquiry without understanding of Indigenous and other cultural perspectives.	Student recognizes that there are Indigenous or other cultural perspectives.	Student shows some consideration of Indigenous or other cultural perspectives.	Student considers holistic perspectives in planning an inquiry.
Performing and Recording • Conducting inquiries • Gathering and recording data	Student shows little interest in and respect for the natural world.	Student makes observations of the natural world.	Student documents observations of the natural world.	Student observes and documents the natural world holistically and with respect.
Analyzing and Interpreting • Analyzing data • Assessing explanations	Student shows understanding that there are different ways of knowing the natural world with significant guidance and support.	Student shows understanding that there are different ways of knowing the natural world with some guidance and support.	Student shows understanding that there are different ways of knowing the natural world independently.	Student considers or proposes explanations of natural phenomena based on Traditional Knowledge.
Communication and Teamwork	Student shows little recognition of oral traditions for communicating wisdom.	Student shows some recognition of oral traditions for communicating wisdom.	Student recognizes oral traditions for communicating wisdom.	Student chooses oral traditions for communicating wisdom.

	Level 1	Level 2	Level 3	Level 4
STSE				
Nature of Science and Technology	Student refers to scientific and other cultural knowledge systems with significant guidance and support.	Student refers to scientific and other cultural knowledge systems with some guidance and support.	Student recognizes both scientific and other cultural knowledge systems and technologies.	Student recognizes and respects both scientific and other cultural knowledge systems and technologies.
Social and Environmental Contexts of Science and Technology • Planning projects • Reporting findings	Student shows little understanding of cultural and environmental connections to science and technology.	Student shows some understanding of cultural and environmental connections to science and technology.	Student shows considerable understanding of cultural connections and environmental considerations to science and technology.	Student shows a hig degree of respect fo and understanding c cultural perspective and environmental considerations to science and technology.
Attitudes				
Collaboration • Planning investigations • Conducting inquiries • Gathering data	Student recognizes that there are Knowledge Keepers.	Student recognizes that Knowledge Keepers may have Traditional Knowledge related to topic of inquiry.	Student recognizes that there are protocols for obtaining knowledge from Knowledge Keepers and sharing it with others.	Student honours protocols for obtaining knowledg from Knowledge Keepers and takes responsibility for having this knowledge.
Appreciation of Science • Planning projects • Reporting findings	Student shows little understanding of the contributions of people from various cultures to understanding natural phenomena.	Student shows some understanding of the contributions of people from various cultures to understanding natural phenomena.	Student recognizes the contributions of people from various cultures to understanding natural phenomena.	Student appreciates and values the contributions of people from various cultures to understanding natural phenomena.
Stewardship Posing questions Planning inquiries • Analyzing data	Student shows little recognition that there is place-based knowledge.	Student shows some recognition that there is place-based knowledge.	Student recognizes place-based knowledge.	Student values plac based knowledge to solve local problem

Name: ______________________

Initiating and Planning

	Level 1	Level 2	Level 3	Level 4
Initiating the Task				
Identifying Topic of Inquiry	Student is not able to identify a question, practical problem, or issue having societal or environmental implications related to the science topic being studied.	Student identifies, with assistance, a topic-related question to answer, a practical problem to solve, or an issue having societal or environmental implications.	Student identifies a topic-related question to answer, a practical problem to solve, or an issue having societal or environmental implications.	Student clearly identifies and refines a topic-related question to answer, a practical problem to solve, or an issue having societal or environmental implications.
Developing Background Knowledge				
Researching Inquiry Problem	Student requires significant support to gain information from appropriate reference sources related to the inquiry problem.	Student requires some support to gain information from appropriate reference sources related to the inquiry problem.	Student is able to gain information from appropriate reference sources related to the inquiry problem.	Student is able to gain information from multiple reference sources related to the inquiry problem.
Planning Inquiry				
Posing Question (if applicable)	Student is able to pose a testable question with significant guidance and support.	Student is able to pose a testable question and predict what will happen with some guidance and support.	Student is able to pose a testable question and predict what will happen independently.	Student poses a testable question, predicts what will happen, and identifies variables.
Planning Procedures				
Creating Inquiry Plan	Student identifies some procedures for the inquiry with significant guidance and support.	Student identifies procedures for the inquiry with some assistance.	Student identifies and records procedures to guide the inquiry.	Student develops a written plan of procedures and materials to guide the inquiry.

Name: ____________________

Performing and Recording

	Level 1	Level 2	Level 3	Level 4
Performing Inquiry				
Implementing Plan	Student implements a prescribed plan with assistance.	Student safely implements a prescribed plan.	Student safely implements his/her own written plan with guidance.	Student safely implements his/her own written plan independently.
Recording Data				
Gathering Evidence	Student collects data using appropriate tools and techniques with significant guidance and support.	Student collects and records data using appropriate tools and techniques with some guidance and support.	Student collects and records data safely using appropriate tools and techniques independently.	Student collects and records data safely using tools and techniques that go beyond what is introduced and modelled in class.
Organizing Data				
Representing Evidence	Student reports data in a modelled format appropriate to the task with significant guidance and support.	Student reports data in a modelled format appropriate to the task with some guidance and support.	Student reports data in a modelled format appropriate to the task.	Student is able to go beyond the modelled format to organize and display data using other modes of representation appropriate to the task.
Refining Inquiry Plan				
Evaluating Plan	Student is able to discuss inquiry plan, prototype construction, or options to develop plan of action with significant guidance and support.	Student is able to discuss inquiry plan, prototype construction, or options to develop plan of action with guidance.	Student is able to assess inquiry plan, prototype construction, or options to develop plan of action with guidance.	Student is able to assess and offer suggestions for refining inquiry plan, refining prototype construction, or clarifying options to develop plan of action independently.

Name: ______________________________

Analyzing and Interpreting

	Level 1	Level 2	Level 3	Level 4
Analyzing Data				
Assessing Evidence	Student identifies some patterns in the data with significant guidance and support.	Student identifies most patterns or relationships in the data with some guidance and support.	Student identifies patterns and relationships in the data that relate to problem, prototype, or issue.	Student identifies patterns and relationships in the data and correctly relates them to problem, prototype, or issue.
Understanding Need for Evidence	Student does not recognize that knowledge in science is based on evidence.	Student recognizes that evidence is needed to develop knowledge in science.	Student understands the need for evidence to develop knowledge in science.	Student clearly understands the need for evidence, ideally quantitative, to develop knowledge in science.
Interpreting Data				
Proposing Explanations	Student proposes explanation of patterns or relationships in the data with significant guidance and support.	Student proposes explanations of patterns or relationships in the data with some guidance and support	Student proposes explanations of patterns and relationships in the data.	Student correctly proposes explanations of all relevant patterns and relationships in the data.
Refining Explanations	Student attempts a new prediction, suggests changes to prototype, or comments on a decision or plan of action with significant guidance and support.	Student makes a new prediction based on data, suggests improvements to the prototype, or assesses the decision or plan of action with some guidance and support.	Student makes a new prediction based on data, suggests improvements to the prototype, or assesses the decision or plan of action based on student-created criteria.	Student makes an insightful prediction based on data, suggests effective improvements to the prototype, or assesses the decision or plan of action considering science concepts.
Considering Context	Student shows little recognition of the need to consider societal and environmental factors when interpreting and reporting on data.	Student recognizes the need to consider societal and environmental factors when interpreting and reporting on data.	Student understands the need to consider societal and environmental factors in proposing explanations, developing technologies, or recommending solutions.	Student understands and incorporates societal and environmental factors in proposing explanations, developing technologies, or recommending solutions.

Name: ______________________

Communication and Teamwork

	Level 1	Level 2	Level 3	Level 4
Communicating				
Expressing Ideas • Various forms of media: text, charts, diagrams, drama, illustrations, photographs, demonstrations, or audio or video recordings	Student uses some conventions, vocabulary, and terminology in oral, written, or visual communication of results with significant guidance and support.	Student uses conventions, vocabulary, and terminology in oral, written, or visual communication of results with some guidance and support.	Student uses conventions, vocabulary, and terminology in oral, written, or visual communication of results independently.	Student effectively uses conventions, vocabulary, and terminology in oral, written, or visual communication of results.
Addressing Audience • Appropriate for target audience: written report, charts and diagrams, oral, or visual format	Student expresses and organizes ideas and information with limited effectiveness, or with significant guidance and support.	Student expresses and organizes ideas and information with some effectiveness, or with some guidance and support.	Student expresses and organizes ideas and information taking audience or purpose of project into consideration.	Student effectively expresses and organizes ideas and information taking audience and purpose of project into consideration.
Teamwork				
Collaborating with Others	Student collaborates little with classmates throughout the inquiry.	Student collaborates occasionally with classmates and sometimes acknowledges the contributions of others.	Student collaborates with classmates throughout most of the inquiry, contributing to the team and listening to the contributions of others.	Student collaborates with classmates through the entire inquiry process, contributing effectively to the team and encouraging and respecting the contributions of others.
Reflection				
Reflecting on the Inquiry Process	Student shows little ability to reflect on the inquiry process and does not suggest ideas for improvement.	Student reflects on some aspects of the inquiry but does not suggest ideas for improvement.	Student reflects on most aspects of the inquiry and suggests few ideas for improvement.	Student reflects on all aspects of the inquiry, including the results obtained, and provides suggestions for improving the process.

Name: ______________________

I Wonder …

Name: ______________________

Let's Predict

1. What are you wondering about?

2. How will you find out?

3. What do you predict will happen?

4. Were you right?

5. What does that tell you about predicting?

Name: ____________________

A Fair Test

1. What do you want to find out about?

2. What materials do you need?

3. How will you make the test fair?

4. What were your test results?

5. What does that tell you?

Name: ______________________

Finding Out

1. I Wonder ...

What are you wondering about?

2. Predict

What do you predict the answer will be?

3. Make a Plan

What do you plan to do to find out?

4. Explore and Test

What did you do?

What did you observe?

Is that what you predicted?

5.Figure It Out

What do you think that means?

Name: ________________

Make a T-chart

Write the names of the two things you are comparing at the top of the chart. Then, use words or pictures to compare them.

Name: ______________________________

A Venn Diagram

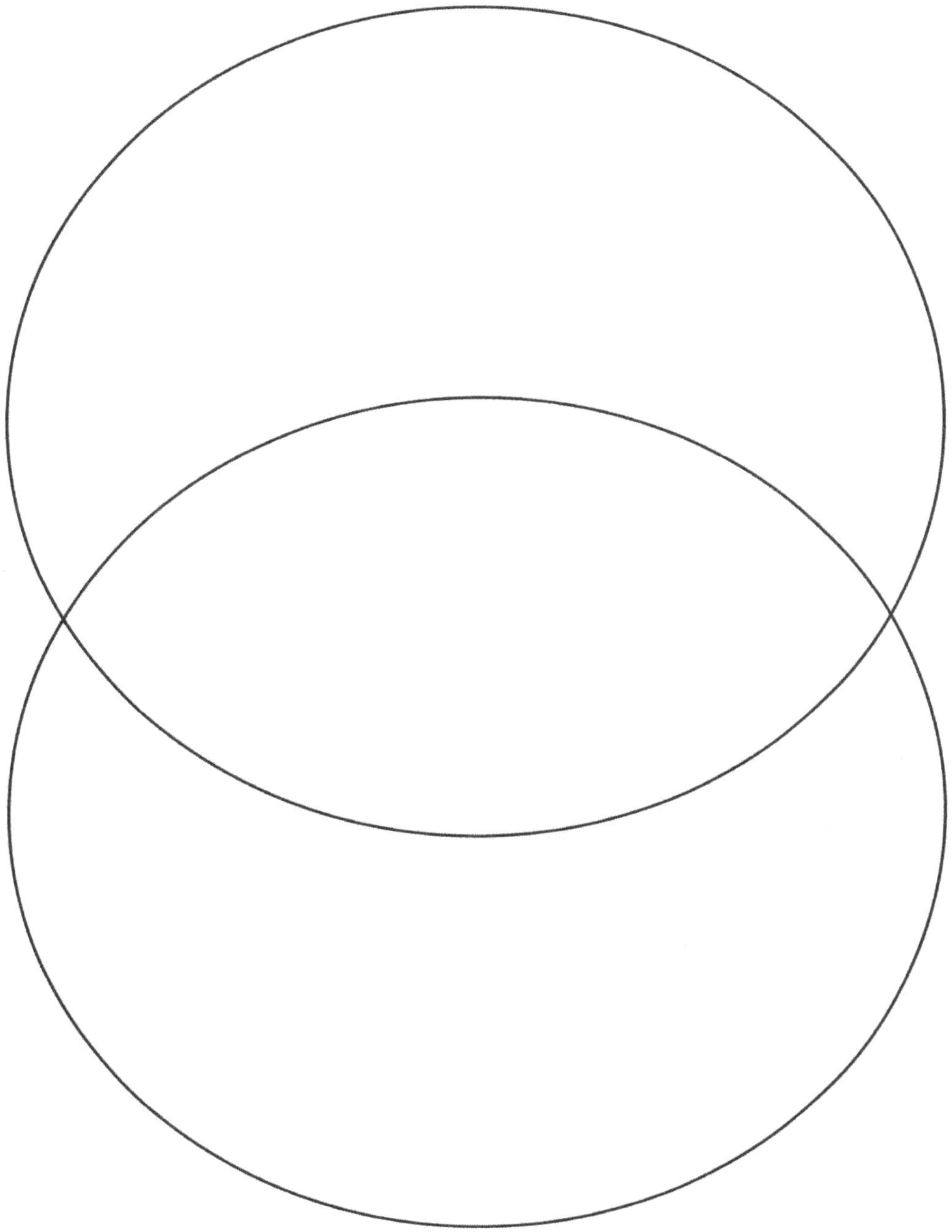

Name: ____________________

Make a Bar Graph

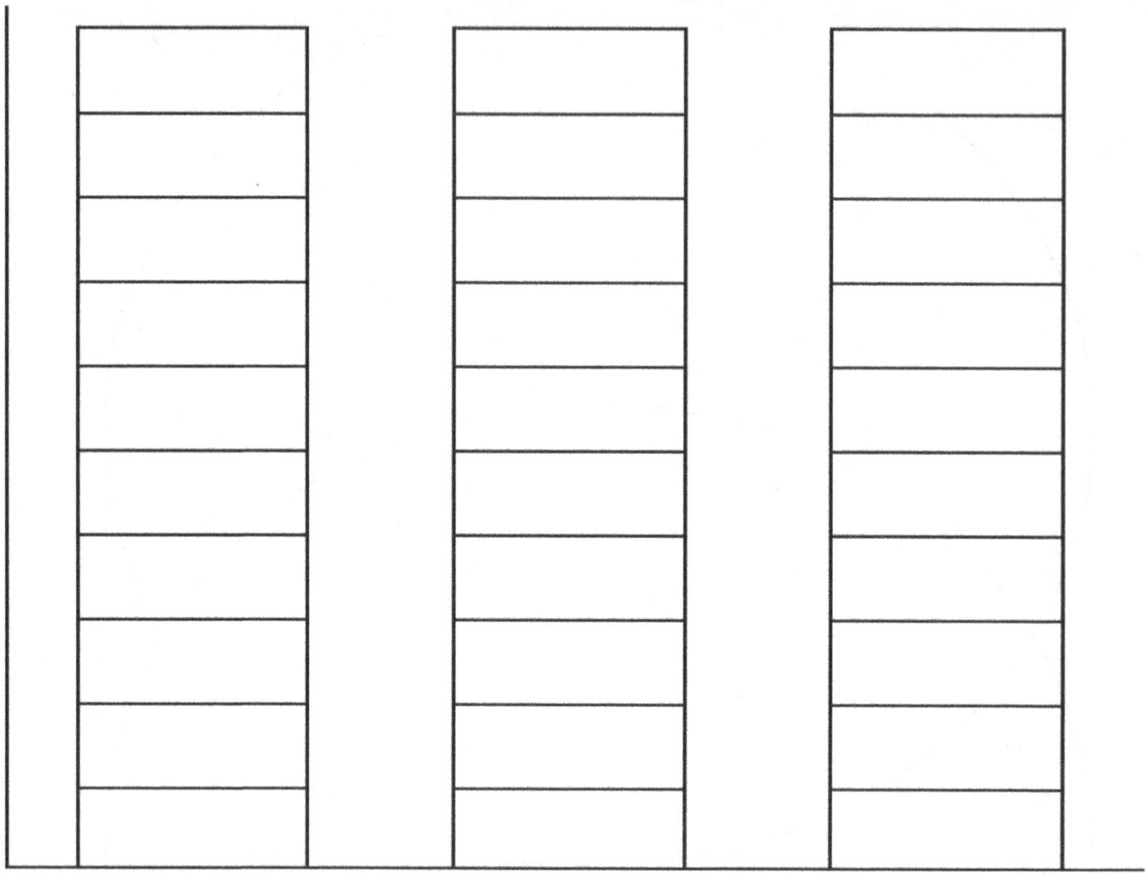

What did you learn from this bar graph?

Name: ____________________

Make a Web

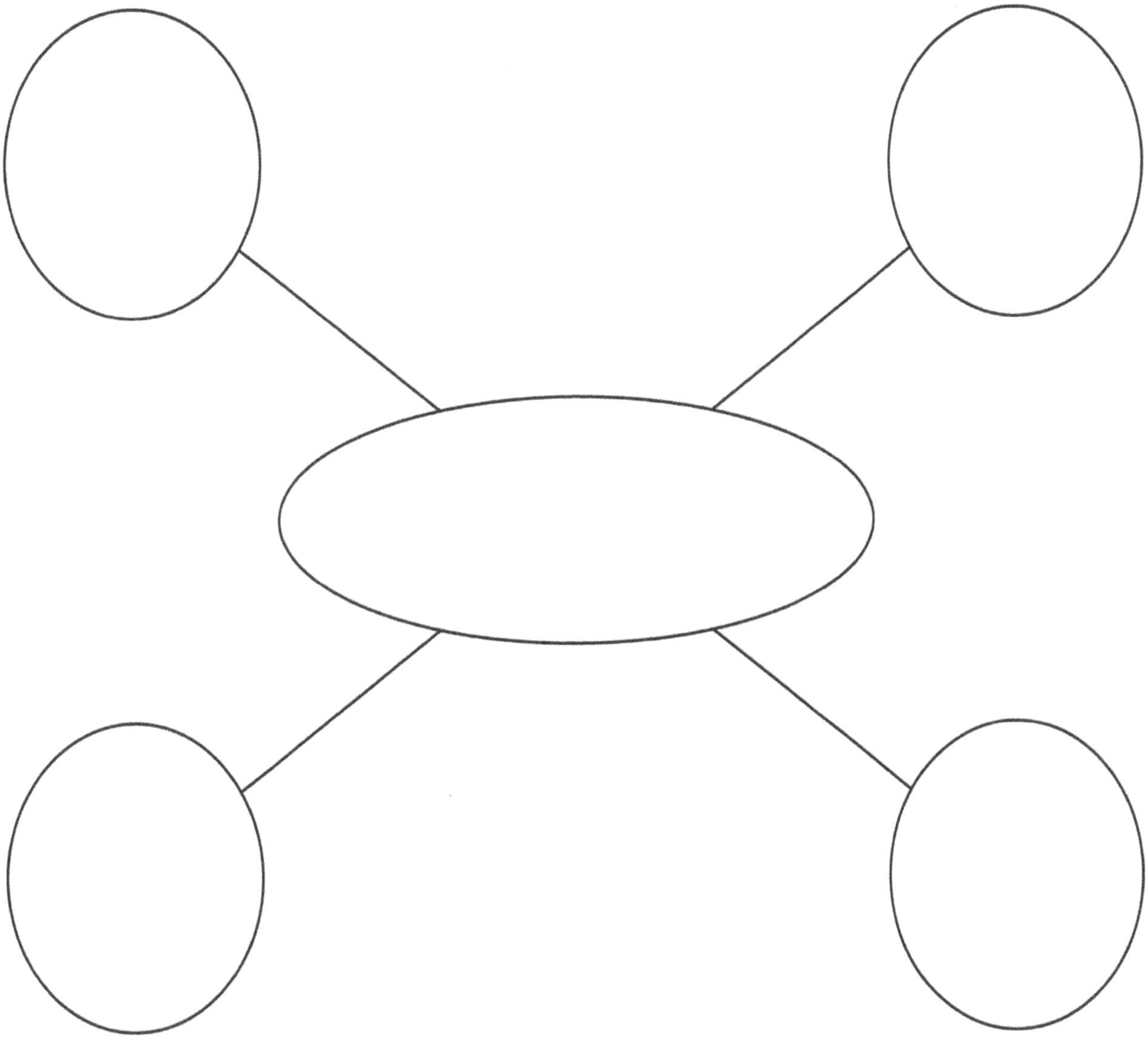

Name: ______________________

I Found Out

This is what I found out...

Name: ______________________________

K-W-L Chart

Topic		
Before Reading	After Reading the Headings and Visual Aids	After Reading
K	W	L
What do we already know?	What do we want to know?	What have we learned or still need to learn?

(adapted from Ogle, 1986)

Name: ______________________

K-W-H-L Chart

Topic			
Before Reading	After Reading the Heading and Visual Aids	After Reading the Heading and Visual Aids	After Readin
K	**W**	**H**	**L**
What we already know?	What do we want to know?	How will we find out the things we want to know?	What we have learned or still ne to learn?

(adapted from Ogle, 1986)

Name: ____________________

A Grid

Name: ____________________

Look What I've Learned

Something I already knew …

Two new things I learned …

Now I wonder…